PATIENT STORIES:

Coping with Life-Changing Illnesses

Andrea King

Thomson Shore rev. date: 06/30/2011

Our website: www.patientstories.com

Printed in the United States of America at Thomson Shore Inc.

ISBN # 978-0-9834-2910-4 (sc)

To my sister, Alaina, who has given me a new definition
of happiness and is truly the purest heart I know.

Contents

ACKNOWLEDGMENTS

With special thanks to Brooks and Linda Gleichert, who made *Patient Stories* possible; Jamie and Sarah Hodges; Hillary Handwerger of TLCI Website Solutions; Kate Hayes and the Noir staff; contributing writer Thelma McDaniel and her co-writer Ken Hill for the stories of Fred Bear, Thelma Bear, Emerson and Fionn Bear, Jamie Bear, Sarah Bear, Ken Bear and Bill Lane; contributing writer Ken Wachsberger for the Ralph Bear story; all the people who shared their stories and knowledge; my family and loved ones; and to you readers, who I can now thank for checking another goal off my list.

INTRODUCTION

For Brooks Gleichert, the idea of *Patient Stories* was a newfound reality when he was diagnosed with chronic lymphocytic leukemia (CLL) in 1996. He was told he wouldn't make it to age sixty-five. But instead of letting panic and fear take over, Brooks took over. He moved into action through exercise, eating healthier, stopping the consumption of alcohol, getting his white blood count back to normal, and most importantly, creating an idea to share his knowledge so that others could also take control of their incurable conditions.

His wife, Linda, was diagnosed with dementia, or Alzheimer's, in 2010. Fortunately, with the help of medication and a daily routine that consists of taking care of her rambunctious but loving Labradors, Linda has maintained most of her health.

All in all, though, an unknown diagnosis or illness can be scary for anyone. That's when Brooks decided to create a website, www. patientstories.com, and this book, to help others in need.

I met Brooks at a local coffee shop, and I remember thinking how excited he was to share his new concept with anyone—and just about everyone in the cafe. And as his luck would have it, he also stumbled upon a seasoned writer that day, who just so happened to share his enthusiasm for the project.

As a journalist for many years, I was used to "pounding the pavement" and meeting with all types of personalities. Today I can proudly say that with my help, we have grown *Patient Stories* into a thriving online database filled with community stories, and we look forward to a future of further web enhancements and books to follow.

In many of the stories, you will discover the "Bear" family name. That's because all the stories are of a personal and private matter, which we wanted to respect by allowing people their anonymity, if they so choose. Thankfully, though, most have agreed to share not only their accounts but their real names. I also wrote each story in first person, keeping true to their actual account, personal story, and the way they have described their situations.

As for myself, I am by no means an expert in health, nor am I a doctor; but I am a person who sees a purpose, a need, and a great reward in *Patient Stories*. I too have close family members who have been affected by a medical diagnosis, including my dad, who is in remission for prostate cancer, and my little sister, who has a mental illness. They, along with many others, struggle with various illnesses each day, so not only is this project a professional accomplishment, it is a personal one too. It brings me great joy to know that I am not only helping the people I love, but also my neighbors and people all over the world I don't know.

Those of us in this book may not be doctors, but we are real people with real-life needs and concerns when it comes to ourselves, our families, and our friends. This book is a way to get the word out about hope, health, and to spread the good—and, unfortunately, sometimes bad—news, with the realities of various chronic diseases and illnesses. Through the help of the community and the Web, I have gathered feature stories from area people who found the need in a project like *Patient Stories*, and a need to share in return. The goal is people helping people and to continue that growth.

Patient Stories is a book, your book, to help family, friends, and everyone around the world share the knowledge about not only the road to recovery but about how to stay along that path any which way you can.

CHAPTER 1

Alzheimer's

Peter Bear

WE HAVE NEVER REALLY HAD much tragedy in our lives; it has been great, and we have been blessed with wonderful relationships. We had never really been "tested" until my father was diagnosed with Alzheimer's disease. That was when the family was really tested.

If you know anything about the disease, you know it can be a very tiring experience, particularly for a man who is eighty-one years old. But his symptoms, such as forgetfulness, were not as cut and dried, because they were interrelated with his previous heart problems.

My father had been a smoker since age twelve, and although he never came down with lung cancer (good genes, I suppose), he had to have a quadruple bypass in 2000. After that, he had three minor strokes, which led to his speech suffering, his wandering around more, and his poor driving. Still, to this day, even though he no longer drives, no one can take his car away from him.

Emotionally, my father has become quieter but experiences fits of rage. He knows something is wrong and that his mind is going, but he feels confused and frustrated. The unexpected rages are what turned us to the medical field for answers. When first diagnosed, the neurologist told us he was in the middle stages of Alzheimer's; at the time, we did not even know what that meant. After reading a few books on the disease, we thought, *Oh my gosh, that is him.*

Physically, my father does not hurt, but emotionally, he does not know how to process information correctly like he used to, and now he seems to talk in circles.

My father is now in the last stages of the disease; he can barely walk or talk, but even so, no one wanted to put him in a nursing home. Currently, my mother is his full-time caregiver, and she has vowed to take care of him until the day she dies. That is what they promised each other. She, along with his family, would rather have him around than in a nursing home.

He has also been experiencing brain seizures lately, so my father takes medication. In turn, it makes him sleep a lot, but at least he is at home. This way, my father can get some peace and quiet and be around the people who love him and take care of him. He may not always remember us, mostly just here and there, but he is considered a medical miracle when he does, because in those various times, he knows who we are. Thankfully, my mother has nurse's assistants to help cook and clean.

As a daughter, you want to do anything you can for your father. Some may call it common sense; I call it *grace.* There is something to be said about the here and now, and I believe you are never given anything you cannot handle. I hold on to that grace and thank God. I do not see good in the tragedy of life and disease, but I know it is there. I do not see God's glory in suffering, yet I know it is there, and it has pulled this family together. Now we just want to be with him. Even the worst of my father's rages I would take just to have him around. You can either accept it or suffer with him, so why not accept it?

A key is having an eye on eternity, because this is just a fading glimpse of it. With that, I have confidence and hope that I will see him and be with him forever. If I did not have a spiritual belief, I do not think I would be doing that well with this right now. That, to me, is the good news.

Dorothey Meyers

Alzheimer's can be explained as a loss of independence, affection, thinking power, and conversation, things of that nature, but Ed had his way of wiggling my toe when I was sitting in my lounge chair and giving me a kiss goodnight. Those were his ways of showing that he cared during his disease.

Before Ed was diagnosed, he became more anti-social, and he could not carry a conversation the same way as before. I could see the signs coming when we were busy traveling. We both had a love of travel, and Ed had a love of music, and we were big campers who traveled around the country by RV. It seemed as if we were always involved in doing something, but then there were little signs of a turn for the worse, things I would catch of his illness, like how he did not want to be as social anymore, yet he was still able to drive everywhere at the time.

Slowly, Ed became more withdrawn. At the time, it did not really sink in, because withdrawal seems to happen with age too. However, I knew something was wrong.

Ed went to see a neurologist, a cardiologist, received a colonoscopy, and even went through a sleep apnea test. A doctor then recommended a psychologist for geriatric testing, who questioned him on his memory through oral and visual tests. After the tests, the conclusion came: he was diagnosed with Alzheimer's at seventy-seven years of age in 2005.

At first I was shocked, and then despair and sadness took over, and I would just cry. It was not the answer I wanted to hear, but he did live another four years thereafter.

Treatment included the medication Aricept and continued visits with the psychologist. We went along, going out here and there. Even at the doctor visits, he was able to joke around with his physician. But 2009 was the cutoff year; that was when things changed and became different. Ed withdrew even more, and sometimes there were days when he did not even want to get out of bed. His language got more aggressive. He started to blame me for things, and he would swing at me (all of which are symptoms of people with Alzheimer's); he just was not Ed anymore.

I would not argue with him, though, because it is not good to do that with people experiencing that disease. I allowed myself to get angry, because that was something I learned to do in my support group. Ed had a couple of episodes that included anxiety attacks as well, so he also took medication for those.

I had in-home care to help with services and even had to call the police a few times (who were so very nice about it) when I needed help after Ed had a fall. He also had other troubles, such as dressing himself, but the major functions were not too bad, and in that way, I feel I was blessed.

After a few years, though, Ed was declining, and it was recommended that hospice come in to help. That was when I started to keep a diary of what was going on. Eventually, it became too hard for him to get out of bed. I believe Ed willed his brain to shut down, and he was giving up. He did, however, open his eyes one last time to look at his family surrounding him; that was his way of saying goodbye. After two weeks of hospice in 2009, he passed away at eighty-one years of age, right before the holidays.

Being a caregiver, you are allowed to cry, you are allowed to be mad, and you often get frustrated because you always want to do what you can to help. You go through a lot of different emotions as your loved one goes through a decline.

I would advise caregivers to find or form a support group, because you will need one in terms of the comparison, information, and love you will receive. Everyone there is suffering and caring in different ways. After some of the support group sessions, I would hear what the other women went through, and in a way, I left feeling lucky about my situation. I also got a lot of information from books and went to grief counseling following his death.

Through it all, Ed always knew who I was and would not forget a face. Everybody is different; it can vary from person to person, at any age, with Alzheimer's, and it can hit lightly or rather hard. But do not get discouraged, and do not argue with your loved one, because it will just disturb the apple cart. Try to get out of the house once in a while, because you have to get out and make time for yourself too. That is vital when you are taking care of someone else.

CHAPTER 2

Arthritis

Peter Bear

I WAS HEADED ON A downward spiral between my diabetes, COPD, being overweight, and having high cholesterol and arthritis. Overall, I was experiencing weakness, aches, pains, and high sugar levels. Basically, it was time to do something.

My daughter approached a nurse about holistic therapy. I went to this nurse and decided to get off all the medication I was on in exchange for a more holistic lifestyle. The natural products help people like me who are dealing with obesity, diabetes, and cardiovascular disease. After doing this for a month, I went back in for lab work, and at first the results came back bad, but when I went back, the results were better. My insulin usage was cut in half and my sugar levels went down. I also had more energy, less aches and pains, and I even went out to get a new job.

My point is, there are alternatives out there if you understand how the body works. This holistic diet has made me more active, which encouraged me to install a swimming pool at my house, gave me the life to get a new job in the school system, and overall, helped me achieve a more active lifestyle. It's unbelievable.

Cholesterol medication can cause a higher risk of becoming a diabetic, and I already was one, so to have my insulin usage cut in half is huge. You have to think nutrition; the doctors are there for advice, but they don't know everything. True health and wellness is not about medication.

❧

Elizabeth Zilke

It has now been about thirty years since a very old doctor at the old Tuxedo Avenue hospital in Detroit diagnosed me with fibromyalgia. At the time, the pain I was experiencing was dismissed by other doctors; but later, along with the pain came a diagnosis of rheumatoid arthritis, all of which I was told was activated by stress.

I found out our autoimmune system activates by fighting our inner system instead of improving it. And, as a side note, I do not have lupus. However, my mother did have lupus, and not so lucky for me, I inherited severe arthritis. Now I live with my rheumatoid arthritis, degenerative arthritis, and fibromyalgia every day.

In the beginning of the chronic pain, I tried over-the-counter medications and creams and then progressed to prescription so-called *miracle pills*, but when your body is not able to tolerate all of that, you turn to cortisone shots, which are only a temporary relief. When those are not effective, the next step is to try a cane or a wheel-walker. I had a joint replacement in my knee too, which has helped some. That experience was traumatic, as I woke up during the operation because I was not fully sedated. It was not painful, but I could hear and see what was going on.

Now I do physical therapy to strengthen my body, along with exercises at home. There are times when the pain level is at a ten (which is peak, on a scale from one to ten), and on a day-to-day basis, the pain remains at an eight. It's mostly there, and not much helps relieve it. My pain ointments smell bad and are only a temporary relief, and the ones with capsaicin (made with chili pepper) are uncomfortable and burn more than the chronic pain does. Not all medicines provide relief to chronic pain; some leave you with headaches, ulcers, high blood pressure, and depression. That's when I ask, Is the cure worse than the disease? I do, however, take some prescription medications, along with vitamins and fish oil supplements.

It's useless when someone asks, How are you doing? because when you tell them you're not so good because of the pain, they often reply, Join the crowd. Now, if asked, I say in all honesty, Do you really want to know or are you just being polite?

A serious result of the degeneration of your muscles is that you are so aware of the pain that you can't concentrate well. This means bumping into things as you're walking due to being rigid and stiff, or even falling. The best way to describe the chronic pain is the reflection of the picture of that infamous clown with a tear coming down his face. You try to put on a happy face, but really, the pain is real and the tears come down inside. I don't want to keep repeating to my family, I really hurt all over, because I have told them over and over again. But heavy chronic pain is hard for some to realize, as no one can understand the pain level we are feeling. As others go on their merry way, we are thinking how we used to be like that at one time. All in all, though, I do my own cooking, laundry, and cleaning, and I want to be able to take care of myself. I don't want to be in a wheelchair.

I'm eighty years old, and I have always been a vibrant and active person. I raised a family, did the housework, including wallpapering and painting for a living, and walked everywhere around the streets of Detroit. I grew up during the Depression, when things were hard. My husband was an alcoholic who gambled our money away, and the children and house maintenance were all in my hands. I had a hard life physically, but even until the early 1990s I was washing laundry the old washboard way. It's hard how the lack of mobility, due to arthritis, can be something that changes your life. But there is hope, but only if you try hard, think positive, and keep your mind

9

active. I keep mine on the go by doing crossword puzzles, Bible study, and the continued love of learning. Also, find a doctor who understands the pain of arthritis and fibromyalgia, and tell them you may need help.

I don't always like to say it, but my faith keeps me going and helps me get through the day. Sometimes when you mention religion, you may as well put your boxing gloves on, but my faith is my own private way to help. I've been told by my doctor that I'll live to be in my nineties, and I said, "As long as I can get on that table and start dancing, I will." Attitude is really what it's all about.

I know if I can strive to go day by day, have an understanding family, and think positively, things will be that much better. As the saying goes, "This too shall pass." You have to fight to keep a positive attitude with this because the pain is never-ending.

Art Canning

Back several years ago, when I was in my fifties, I noticed I was having trouble running. Eventually, it became difficult not only to run but to maintain other exercise as well.

At the time, the doctor detected arthritis in my left knee that was deteriorating the bone, which led to the "no more running" order, which also meant no exercise that caused a lot of pressure on my knees. But it was no big deal. I just switched to biking to remain active. However, as time went on, I noticed even walking to and from the shopping center was getting to be hard. I could barely make the trip from my car into the store without having to stop, sit down, and rest. It progressively got worse.

Knee replacement being a possibility was not a new concept, seeing as my mom had problems with hers and waited far too long to have her knee and hip replaced. I was most certainly skeptical of the operation because of what I had witnessed, but it finally got to a point where walking a short distance left a constant ache; not so much pain but more like that nagging feeling you have with a toothache. To combat this I took ibuprofen, but it only gave me minor relief. It wasn't until it became obvious after a couple of years, and through my wife's steady reminders, that I needed a knee operation.

I had never had any operations prior to this, so I did a lot of research to find the best in the field, someone with great credentials. In fact, before this operation, I was never really sick. I never even considered I might need an operation (as many men tend to think). I took myself to the Huron Valley Hospital in Michigan and told them I needed to see a doctor with the earliest appointment. He turned out to be an easygoing doctor with a great bedside manner. He took X-rays and asked a lot of questions about my family medical history. The doctor recommended a medication called Stupak to consider before the operation, but it would only give me temporary relief. I researched Stupak and took the medicated shots three times, once a week, into my knee. It posed swelling and complications, but within the first go, I had relief within a week that lasted an entire year. I was pleased, but then when it wore off, I decided to have another set of treatments. This series only lasted nine months. I then had one more series of treatments, but its healing power only lasted six months, and a fourth treatment got me through my vacation time. The doctor said I should tell him when I needed the operation, and that time finally came when I was sixty-four in 2004.

The knee operation went well, and I felt comfortable with the procedure because of the doctor, the informational seminar, and the fact that I made sure to ask a lot of questions about how I could help myself. I was even able to joke around with the medical staff and remain in good humor about the process.

Prior to surgery, I made arrangements to rent a hospital bed at home, which made living downstairs easier. I also had in-house physical therapy for a month. However, I thought it was worthless and disappointing, because my therapist would spend about fifteen minutes doing paperwork instead of investing time on the actual physical therapy. I investigated beforehand though and found Health Styles Rehabilitation, where I still go today for their facilities, exercises, and knee massages. I also spent twelve weeks doing physical therapy in Arizona.

Eventually, I woke up one day and the aches had subsided, which meant everything was getting better in my knee. It was a healing process, and thereafter I used a walker for stability and a cane for comfort. In 2008, it was time to have the second surgery on my right knee. Again, this meant the medicated shots before the actual surgery. The operation went well, besides some minor constipation. I elected to go to rehab this time for sixteen days, which was a great amount of therapy (a full hour in the morning and afternoon) yet fun. Walking was even part of the rehabilitation, because if you don't use your muscles, they will start to deteriorate on you.

Besides the occasional flare-ups due to weather changes, and slight trouble bending, my knees feel good with their plutonium implants. You do have to endure some pain in the knee for stretching purposes and to get your ligaments to heal while doing exercises to help loosen the joints. You also have to get up, walk, and exercise for the rest of your life. I still use exercise machines, do my leg lifts, and ride a bike. In a pinch, bags of frozen peas, some ice, and a heating pad are also instant relief for the knees. My advice is to walk as much as possible and spend the extra money on a good pair of walking shoes.

As for people who have to go through this, make a list of questions, because once you get to your doctor's appointment, you'll forget what to ask. Don't be afraid to ask anything because it's your body. I strongly recommend rehabilitation centers that are close to your home for easier access for you and your family. Also, look into a shuttle service from the hospital and seek equipment from the doctor to help with the rehabilitation afterward. There are things out there to help you, but you have to ask. Spend the time becoming familiar with all aspects of the operation. Read literature, go to the library, and don't become intimidated because the doctor has a degree and is wearing a white coat. Be sure to know what's happening, because there are no dumb questions.

Without my operations, I know I would be bound to a chair right now, unable to get around—not so much from aches and pains, but more from exhaustion. My lifestyle before was different, but now, overall, it's better. And if you recognize other people going through these circumstances, offer assistance.

Colleen Bear

I didn't remember falling or even bumping my knee, but what I did remember was the pain that sent me to my primary care doctor.

I was diagnosed with osteoarthritis and was told I would eventually need a knee replacement sometime down the road. For starters, I worked on exercising the sore joints and took a series of shot medications (about nine months total), but it soon got to the point where I no longer wanted to continue with the injections. Instead, I opted to get the surgery because I just wanted to feel better.

When I was diagnosed, I thought I had an "old-fogie" disease and there was nothing they could do, but when they told me about surgery, I wasn't hesitant at all. Because really, there was nothing else at that point.

My nerves subsided once I attended a two-hour surgery preparation class. Now I tell people that was the best thing I ever did. It explained what ailment I have, showed what my knee looked like and what it would look like once I had the surgery, and it gave tips about what to expect. Prior to this, I had heard horror stories from my sister about a machine that stretched your leg and was extremely painful. I also ran into friends who gave me input and lent me rehabilitation equipment. I took the tips, got the consensus, and did my homework. This all helped take away the fear and give me a positive attitude. Sometimes that can be easier said than done, yet it can be done. I knew I would have to go through a lot, but the end result would be worthwhile.

My surgery went well, and a couple of days later, I was able to go home. My doctor didn't recommend a rehabilitation stay, because at home, I would be forced to help myself recover. What's the worst that could happen? I could get an infection or fall, but I did what I needed to in order to prevent those things. I wasn't in any pain, and little by little I moved my foot around, started walking, and always made sure to eat a lot of healthy foods to help me regain or keep my strength. I also had a lot of great neighbors nearby who would help out and bring me food.

My in-home therapy lasted only a couple of days, and following that, I went to the Michigan Rehabilitation Center three times a week for about two months. They were excellent; they too gave me tips to avoid swelling, and they helped monitor the pain. I can recall giving the therapist a hard time, saying, "I can't," but I eventually gave in, stopped complaining, and did the exercises. At home, I made things work. Doing the laundry meant going up and down stairs. I also got into the habit of walking on my own and used bed props to lift up my bed, which I still use today.

The doctor forewarned me that the day would come when I would need my other knee replaced too. That day arrived at work, two years later, when I went to turn and felt a sharp pain hit me with a zap. It took me about fifteen minutes to walk to my car in the parking lot, and that's when I knew it was time for another surgery.

I chose September and was back to work again in December. This time around, I did slip and fall (luckily, I didn't hurt my knee), and had an allergic reaction to the anesthesia (where I needed a blood transfusion), but otherwise, the surgery went well. If I could take the knowledge of a few minor mistakes that were made and put them into both surgeries, that would be the best of both worlds.

I also discovered personal tips along the way to make the process easier, including adjustments and props around the house, like a higher toilet seat, and a stool for the bathtub. I also don't sit on anything too soft; that way I won't have a terrible time getting back up.

Before, you could tell I had knee problems, but now, you can't even tell when I walk. I've heard a few things that can cause osteoarthritis, like exercising the wrong way, predisposition, or being overweight. Everybody has a theory. What is important is to keep moving and follow what the doctors say, because they give you the tools and then you have to use them. Continually do your exercises. I do mine at the senior center at least twice a week. I also start my day with leg lifts and stretch throughout the day so that I am not in a stationary position.

From what I was told, due to the pain and bone damage, I could have gotten to a point where I was in a wheelchair, and I didn't want that to happen. Every day they are consistently coming out with new medications, but try your best to do some form of exercise each day. That's what I do. Now, I'm not in any pain. I can walk up and down stairs, which is something I had forgotten about. But now, I can do that. I can go on walks. I can do a lot. You don't want to think you can't; you need to be able to do it. I have volunteered in hospice for many years, and seeing what those people went through made me think how my situation was not so bad; it gives you a different perspective.

If it had not been for my sister and friends, who's to say I wouldn't be like the rest of them? How do you get a positive attitude? You become prepared and you think, *I can*. Also, have someone you can call on, even if it is just to say hello, to leave a voicemail checking on how you're doing, or for them to know you exist because it makes a world of difference.

CHAPTER 3

Autism

Jenny Bear

TIMES ARE HARD WITH AUTISM, but they're even harder as a mother of a son with autism. One thing that does help, however, is to cry and get it all out.

The signs with Luke, who is now four years old, came on when he was an infant. As a baby, he had extreme colic, and he did not even recognize me as his mother until he was six months old. As a mother, that was a really hard challenge to not even have your own baby know who you are. From there he never really developed his speech. The pediatrician did not want to tell me what could have been wrong with Luke. Rather, he simply told me that we might want to get him tested for special therapy, stating we could also get assistance through the state.

It was not until his third birthday that we even knew what autism was. Yes, we had heard about it and thought maybe it could be a possibility, but we did not know a lot about it. And no one wanted to tell us what Luke might have, or what he had at all. The best we did hear, however, was from the therapist we were working with, who told us to get Luke diagnosed before the state assistance program was over.

So we did, and Luke was diagnosed within minutes with autism. The doctors knew right away what it was.

From there I did a lot of research and "biomedical protocol checks" for allergies. It turned out Luke was allergic to airborne allergies, like pollens and molds, and was put on supplement therapy and exercises. He also has difficulty running very fast because of his legs and coordination, but we have seen some improvement because of the supplement therapy, which takes the allergies out of his diet. Luke is also hypoglycemic.

Through lots of therapy to help him learn to look, watch, and listen to people, he learns things, such as how to respond when his name is called, and the ability to pull speech out of him. Luke was also put on a low-dose naltrexone (LDN) to increase the endorphins in his body and help boost his immune system. This gives him a more balanced life and schedule.

The LDN was something I researched because it is common for children with autism to have a yeast overgrowth. Autistic children get a lot of opportunist infections, and we saw a lot of yeast come out of him as a result. On the other hand, Luke had a bad reaction at first, so we also tried Diflucan. I worked with an internal medicine doctor where I explained I would be doing the research and making the decisions where Luke's health was concerned, and the doctor would assist me. The LDN medication we found after was something safe that I wanted to try with Luke.

We are still working on things, but the best thing to do is to keep an open mind because it helps your own mind. You try your best to solve it, fix it, and help him recover so he can succeed.

I do not think I would have a son right now without the treatment we are doing. We will continue to do this as Luke continues to interact more and be more responsive, and he even looks at us, his parents, now.

As parents of an autistic child, take matters into your own hands, be responsible for your own treatment, and find a doctor who can listen. Also, keep up daily therapy for both physical and mental well-being.

The condition is long-term and will take time, consultation, and a lot of working through, but just take it one day at a time. That is the best way I know how to do things.

CHAPTER 4

Breast Cancer

Karen Collareno

AS A YOUNG MOTHER, CAN you imagine hearing the words, "You have breast cancer"? So many thoughts go through your head, like, *I'm not going to live to see my children graduate high school,* and *Am I going to live or die?*

I was diagnosed in March 1998, and now I am forty-nine years old, in remission, and cancer free.

Looking back, the symptoms were almost nonexistent, except for the feeling that something was not quite right. I felt exhausted but did not think much of it as a mother who was busy taking care of her small children. However, that feeling of uncertainty, and heart palpitations, made me go to the doctor's office for a physical. The entire test came back fine, but that feeling of uncertainty did not go away, and I knew something was still wrong.

At the same time, a good friend of mine had breast cancer, and I had found a lump in my breast. I kept an eye on it because I was still feeling run down, and the hunch that something was not right would not go away. After a mammogram, I received a letter in the mail stating from the surgeon that the lump needed to be biopsied. However, I was reassured that since I was so young, the chances it was not cancer was good, and that possibly it was just breast tissue. But I did my research and compared a picture of my lump to a picture of a malignant tumor, and they looked similar.

I tried to tell myself not to freak out, and so did the doctor. She even bet her paycheck it was nothing, although she did say she would not bet her son. However, I knew. I knew something was wrong, and after the biopsy results they too knew it was indeed cancer.

Following the results, the tumor was removed and my margins were clear, meaning the cancer had not spread into my lymph nodes. Even after all that, though, I still received chemotherapy for six months and radiation treatment for thirty days. Luckily, the chemotherapy was not an aggressive type. Yes, I lost my hair, was weak, and went into early menopause—things were tough—but I had a great group of family and friends to support me. I am glad I did the radiation, even while others told me not to. I was young and wanted to throw everything I could at this disease. The radiation was not so bad either, kind of like having a sunburn. It can be pretty amazing what you can get through when you have to, and I certainly did a lot of praying.

I also received a Tamoxifen treatment, which is mainly used for arthritis patients but was also found to help fight breast cancer. It turned out for me, however, that I did not respond well during the two years of that treatment and as a result had vaginal bleeding. I got off the medication and listened to my body, once again.

Now I go in for a checkup once a year, do a monthly breast exam, exercise, and try to eat well. I would say listen to your body, go out and find what is going on, and do your due diligence. My lifestyle was not always about that, and the further out you get, the more you tend to get complacent. Not that being complacent is a good thing, but it happens. People get busy. Also, remain educated on the disease and try to eliminate stress in life; I believe that stress can be a cause of cancer.

Before I was diagnosed with breast cancer, I think my life was passing me by because I got caught up in the everyday things, but when you are diagnosed with an illness, all that changes, and none of that matters. It forces you to do things in a different light.

I decided to volunteer at the hospital after my treatment because I wanted to be there for women like me, to tell them it was going to be okay. Most importantly, though, do not let yourself become complacent, remember to stay focused, and always remember what is important.

Without my treatment, I would constantly be looking in the mirror, wondering about my disease, and not having the piece of mind I do today. I would say reevaluate your life and really concentrate on the important things, do not sweat the small stuff, live for today, and listen to your body.

୧ଛ

Cheryl Prowse

Throughout the whole process, and for my story, faith is so important. To me, it's all about that because my testimony is my faith.

There were no symptoms of my breast cancer, but after a yearly mammogram in 2005, my doctor at Beaumont Hospital in Michigan scheduled a core biopsy. During the time I was waiting for the results, my dad fell and broke his hip, and even though I was uncertain of my biopsy results, there was no time to worry about myself because I was so involved with helping my parents. Even when I was diagnosed at fifty-eight with a malignant tumor in my breast, my stuff didn't seem like anything.

Three weeks later, I discovered it was stage one cancer, found early, but when I went for the surgery to remove the tumor, it was found to be an aggressive form that had moved into my lymph nodes. This advanced my diagnosis to stage-two cancer, and not only was the tumor removed, but fourteen lymph nodes were as well.

Since my cancer was an aggressive form, treatment included chemotherapy and radiation, with chemotherapy first. The doctors wanted to use the strongest medicine they had to fight, which meant six applications every three weeks. I have always been in good shape, loved to exercise, and was even an aerobics instructor for many years. Once the doctor told me I was in excellent health, in every other way, that made the first session very emotional. I luckily began in a strong position and had no qualms about doing this bout of strong chemotherapy.

It turns out I was wrong. After this first dose of chemotherapy, I ended up in the hospital with a life-threatening gastrointestinal reaction from the medication Taxotere. Anyone who has been through breast cancer would know this medication. For me, this was a near-death experience.

After five days, I couldn't eat or hold anything in my system. It was all coming out, and it wouldn't stop; mind you, I was also extremely dehydrated. The hospital believed I had an intestinal infection and found out through blood work that my white blood cells were almost zero. Basically, all the vitamins and minerals were being drained out of my body. I was immediately put into isolation where I stayed for the next twelve days.

I had IVs hooked up to my arm with ten or twelve bags of fluids going into me, and my body was depleted of potassium. The doctors were also fearful that I was going to go into cardiac arrest. My faith, however, helped me to believe I was going to be okay, and that helped me to try and make it by each day. By about day six, a lab technician looked at me and told me how he normally doesn't visit patients but he had to see me because of how sick I was. I laughed, because for the first time, he was the only one who was honest with me. He knew what I needed, which was a pick line that went directly into my blood stream; it was either that or I would die.

At the same time, my hospital room was a revolving door of family and friends from church. I always had someone in there going through the process with me. By day seven, though, my body broke down, and I went into convulsions. I can remember my daughter watching as my sister started praying for me, but I had an out-of-body experience. I believe my spirit went to heaven, a beautiful place filled with vibrant colors, comforting sounds, and singing. I didn't want to go back to my body, but I did. I received medication to put my body back in control, and the next night, I had my daughter, her husband and friends from church come in to pray for healing. I felt as if a heavy lead blanket was being lifted off me, as if someone just removed fifty pounds. My heart started beating more regularly, my vision cleared, and I felt as if I was healed. I could even feel the thickness in the room fall until it became peaceful, blissful, and beautiful. And even though I had lost fifteen pounds and my hair was gone, people told me I was glowing. Even my daughter's husband, who's not a big believer in religion, felt it was a miracle.

The next day, my doctor asked what happened, and I told him, "Jesus healed me," and my doctor said, "I'll take it." A week later, I was able to eat and walk around, and everyone seemed amazed. I eventually built up speed and each day improved to the point where I had my gym shoes on and was almost running. The doctor told me I was an inspiration, but I never looked at it that way. I just wanted to go home. Three days later, I did.

Professionally, I had a physically demanding job working with plants, and I never missed a day while I finished my chemotherapy, which was difficult. After about a month, I started radiation for about thirty-five treatments. Since I have always been physically active, I wanted to prove to myself that I could still run, even through chemotherapy. So every Saturday, I would go out for my four-mile run. I was shocked, but I did it, and my doctor called me his superstar chemotherapy patient.

Shortly after, I was laid off from my job, but I needed to work. I needed insurance, and I was stuck. But I got my answer when I received a position as an environmental attendant at Beaumont Hospital. I feel I was guided to talk to patients and give them positive food for thought to inspire them, give them my story, and whatever they needed for positive word.

It took a long time to heal from the surgery, chemotherapy, and radiation, but I didn't want to baby myself, I wanted to build my body on my own, and on my schedule. I began running on a regular basis, went to the gym, did stretches, and continued my massage therapy work. When I think about doing massage therapy still, even through my treatments, what I've been through is kind of unbelievable. For me, it was important to get back into the routine of being me.

Through it all, I didn't let the cancer and treatment run my life, because that was a part of my life I wanted to get away from. I wanted my life to be me, and then, once I was over the hurdle, I could help motivate others. Some people get so consumed when they are diagnosed with an illness, but for me, it was in my back pocket; it wasn't who I was.

When you go through the whole process of losing your hair and losing your feeling of femininity and feeling pretty, like many women do, it can be difficult, but I tried not to worry about that. I made light of it because I had to.

In any given situation, seeing all that and being in a hospital on a regular basis, I don't believe people can go through this alone. For me it was faith, and I praise the Lord for helping me get through this bump in the road. I've been in remission for five years, and I'm still working, exercising, taking care of my dad, and receiving my yearly mammogram. I feel healed, strong, healthy, happy, and at the point where I can be an inspiration to others. Life now means I can be more open, where I can share my experiences and be there to listen. I've also gotten a lot closer to people who mean a lot to me because I see what's really important.

I feel a little bit of humility goes along with this, but positivity is a big thing, and I see this experience as a good thing, not a bad one. People have to dig really deep into themselves to see who they are, and they have to believe and have faith. The people close to you will want to help, so let them help, and accept what you need. The sky's the limit, and wherever it takes me from here, I'm going; nothing's going to hold me back.

CHAPTER 5

Cerebral Palsy

Jonathon Collareno

HONESTLY, I AM REALLY GRATEFUL for my parents, coaches, doctors, and everyone who has done something for me to help my cerebral palsy. I will be in debt to them forever, now because they made all those places a happy time for me. I say this because now, at age nineteen, I hope to graduate from college with a degree in finance, play men's club rugby, and continue to stay active.

As a twin, my brain did not receive enough oxygen when I was born, and there was a tube in my brain that had grown smaller than it was supposed to. This is what caused my cerebral palsy, and it will never go away.

When I was young, the signs of my condition came out in my speech. I stuttered and was not pronouncing words correctly. Athletic-wise, I could not run, and really, I was not very flexible. I definitely knew I was different from everyone else, that was obvious with my speech, but my parents noticed too, and they brought me to a specialist.

From then on, as an eight-year-old child in the third grade, I experienced two years of physical therapy, about a year and a half of occupational therapy, and thirteen years of speech therapy. I also wore splints to stretch my calves and to stop me from walking on my toes, forcing me to walk normal. It turns out everything worked out fabulously.

The physical therapy worked well, and I learned martial arts, but what really helped was swimming. Of course being athletic and physically fit helped the cerebral palsy, but to be honest, I hated swimming; I just couldn't get into it. I wanted to play football, and at that point, I was physically ready for it. As it turns out, after seventh grade, I was (physically) fine.

Today I run almost every day. I lift weights, and I'll be playing rugby in college. I also continue to see a speech teacher. It is there, at speech therapy, that I use a technology that enables a device in my ear to send a robotic voice off, forcing me to talk slower and allows for help with my speech.

Without the treatments and steps I have been through, it would be tough. I wouldn't be able to run, I wouldn't be able to play football, I wouldn't have a social life, and there would be no dating for me. I wasn't so *normal* before, and now I'm more social. I would tell people like me to definitely get involved in a sport, and listen to the doctor and do what he or she says. Also, stretch at home, continue physical therapy, and stay positive.

Before I was diagnosed, I always felt different, and people would make fun of me because of my speech. It would bother me, but now people don't even notice. I speak a lot better now; it's still not great, but there are parts you learn to live with. However, if you do what the doctors say, everything will fix itself.

CHAPTER 6

Colon Cancer

Leon Keller

IT WAS 1975 WHEN I was diagnosed with colon cancer, but the funny thing was, there were no symptoms. I did not even know I had cancer.

I went in for a routine exam, and they found polyps in my colon. From there, I was referred to an oncologist, who wanted to perform surgery to remove a portion of my large intestine. However, at the time, my wife suggested we try another method, another option of treatment as opposed to surgery. Instead, we went to the Reno Integrative Medical Center in Nevada to see a holistic doctor.

Dr. Douglas Brodie was well-known for treating cancer patients in an alternative way through homeopathics, such as vitamins and herbal preparations. I took part in this treatment and turned to a macrobiotic diet with lots of vitamins to fight the cancer out of my system. My new diet meant quitting smoking and consuming no meat. Yes, that means eating no animals and eating only all-natural foods that can be found at stores like Whole Foods. I did this method of treatment for three months, and when I went back to see the doctor, I was told my polyps were gone and so was the cancer.

In my opinion, I wonder why the Cancer Society hasn't followed through on treatments like this. My holistic treatment worked for me, and I have been cancer free ever since. For this I really give credit to my wonderful wife for persuading me to see this doctor in the first place.

Now I continue my diet and rarely eat meat, also thanks to my wife, who was a terrific cook and person. I eat smaller portions of food, and even my desserts were (and are) altered to have a lower amount of sugar, and that is what I keep track of month to month.

I grew up on the lake, worked hard every day, and tried to get a lot of exercise, and for someone who is eighty-eight years old, I still drive, do housework, and get around pretty well.

I didn't even realize I had colon cancer until they found it, but that was when I did things differently, not only in regard to eating and taking vitamins, but activity-wise; I did everything I usually did. These methods of treatment worked for me, so I say, find a doctor like mine and don't let the doctors cut instantly. At the very least, get another opinion or two.

Lynn Dransfield

I am one of the fortunate ones. The reason I put it that way is that I was diagnosed with colon cancer about thirteen years ago and have been cancer free since my treatment.

I did not really have any symptoms, but when I went back to the doctors for a physical, my blood count was low. Originally, I was tested for an ulcer, but then I went in for a colonoscopy, and that was when a large tumor was found.

I remember when they called to tell me it was cancer. I had to sit on the couch for a while because it was all so overwhelming to me, but then I thought, *I am not going to think of it that way, as cancer,*

I am going to get better. I never want to be frightened by this again, I thought, and I was going to get better, and I did.

I had the operation to remove the tumor and had chemotherapy for the six months that followed. Also, I ate well (maybe too well) and took care of myself. Another trick to staying healthy, which I started during my chemotherapy treatments, was that whenever I came back from somewhere—the store, an appointment, wherever—I always ran in and washed my hands. In chemo, you have to be really careful you don't get sick because you are so darn weak; this is something I still do today when I come back from anywhere. I was also scared of losing my hair during the chemo treatments, but I did not lose it all, it just got a little thinner.

Now, at seventy-six years old, I can happily say that the last time I went in for a check-up there was one polyp, but I was told it would never turn into cancer.

I do not think I would be here now if it was not for this treatment. They took out eighteen of my lymph nodes and it was serious, that I know, but I was lucky. I was lucky the doctor found the cancer and that I went back for a colonoscopy. The funny thing is, prior to that when I went in for a check-up, I remember the doctor telling me he did not think he would see me again.

I recommend getting your colonoscopy when you are supposed to, even if you fear them, like I did. Out of fear, I shied away from it, but it really was not that bad. The hard part is the preparation before, because you cannot eat, and the liquid you have to drink tastes terrible. It may not be a pleasant three days before, but the colonoscopy itself is easy because you are put to sleep.

I do not really think my lifestyle was any different before, but now, things are good.

CHAPTER 7:

Cystic Fibrosis

Emily Schaller

I HAVE ALWAYS BEEN POSITIVE and optimistic, even seeing the positive side about my cystic fibrosis; it's never really gotten to me. I'm not afraid of dying, either, because I'm confident I'm going to live a long time, and for that, I have the Cystic Fibrosis Foundation to thank because they are main reason I am alive.

Cystic fibrosis (CF) is a genetic disorder that causes thickened, sticky mucus, which clogs the vital organs—in particular, the lungs and the pancreas. I was diagnosed when I was just eighteen months old. My parents noticed chronic ear infections and a failure to thrive. I would eat a lot of food yet was not gaining a lot of weight. That's when my parents knew something was wrong. At the time, I think my parents felt scared and freaked out because patients with CF were not living as long; people didn't know as much about the disease. But I thank my parents for letting me be like every other kid.

A pediatrician sent me to get tested for CF through a "sweat test" that checks the sodium and chloride levels in your body. This disease affects the lungs and digestive system; however, the test came back negative, which is also common.

I still wasn't gaining weight though, and I was growing prone to ear infections. Although the disease mostly affects the lungs, it is also part of the digestive system, so I would eat a meal and it would come right out. This time when I was tested yet again for CF, the test came back positive for the disease, which meant the start of pancreatic enzymes to help my body absorb the vitamins from food, increase weight gain, and of course, get me back on a healthy track.

From there I was able to stay active and would only go in for check-ups until about twelve years old. It was then that doctors started to notice an abnormal cough with more mucus, which they wanted to treat as a lung infection. I started taking IV drugs and antibiotics for my CF and eventually added a daily twenty-minute breathing regimen to my routine. The older I got, the more medications I added to ward off and keep the infection at bay, and the more successful I am at that, the healthier I am to fight.

Through my mid teens, the CF progressed and left me in the hospital about two to three times a year. I also happened to be allergic to just about every antibiotic there is to treat my lungs. In a sense, it was nice to miss a lot of school at the time, but some of the hospital stays lasted several weeks, depending on the breathing tests and my lung function. Now I know if my lung function goes down, and it feels harder for me to breath, it's time to get treatment; basically, I know when I need a tune-up.

You get to know yourself and your body well. You also get to the point where you tell the doctors what you need. Every year following, about two to three times a year, I was in and out of the hospital. After high school, I laid off exercise and played in a band. Really, I just didn't make exercise a priority, but then I thought, *Maybe if I start running it would help.* I entered a 5K race and noticed my lung function increase so I ran more, started biking, and didn't need as many medications or hospital visits.

Now it is about maintenance. I wear an electric vest, which helps shake the mucus out of my lungs because airway clearance is important. If the mucus sits in your lungs, it can cause infection and lung damage, so the point is to wear this vest when needed to help get the mucus out. I also stay ahead of my CF, along with breathing treatments for one to two hours, and a daily pill to treat the cause before the symptoms and daily enzymes. I also eat a ton to maintain weight, but it's a vegetarian diet consisting of whole foods, which is easier to fight CF with and stay healthy.

I recently lost a friend with CF who was only thirty-two years old. She'd had a double lung transplant several years ago but her body rejected the organ. Knowing that, even going through that makes me hopeful, though, because now I'm on a clinical trial for a medication, and I have never seen my pulmonary lung function this high; I've never felt this good. There have been leaps and bounds with the treatment of CF, and while the life expectancy is about thirty-eight years, if we can get this medication approved, people can start taking the medication as a young child and live even longer.

Personally, I feel thirty-eight is just a number. I think the message here is hope. It is believed that within five years, 90 percent of CF patients will have a pill to control their disease. Without all these treatment options, I would be sick. I could have had a lung transplant, but I wouldn't have the quality of life I have now. Now I run about twenty-five to thirty miles a week, do my treatments, eat a high-calorie diet, and get at least eight hours of sleep each night. You only have one body, so you have to take care of it.

It all comes back to hope. You do what you have to do to get through the day, but in the near future, there will be even more to improve the quality of life for CF patients. I can't picture my life without CF. I always think, *What would I be doing if I didn't have it?* Probably the typical American thing, of college after high school and an entry-level job, but I like what I'm doing now: guest-speaking about the disease, running marathons, and working with my foundation, Rock CF.

❧

Kim Wilk

My parents noticed symptoms when I was four years old, such as the clubbing of fingernails, diarrhea, salty skin, and not being able to digest my food properly. I was tested for cystic fibrosis (CF), but the results initially came back negative.

When I was eight, I went back to the doctors for what they thought was allergies; however, I was diagnosed with borderline CF. The thing is, with CF, it's a gray scale, and not everyone is the same. Some have it in the lungs and some in the pancreas; however, I have both. I can imagine my parents felt scared when I was diagnosed, but it got them to quit smoking at least, so that was a plus.

After I was diagnosed, I was put on enzymes, and as I got older, I received further treatments and medications. Once that happened, I was able to digest food and gain weight, and the diarrhea stopped too. I was also put on medication to prevent infections. Another effect of CF is that 8 percent of us develop diabetes; it depends on the person, but I developed it at age thirteen.

With CF, the body produces too much mucus, which is thick, sticky, and everywhere in your body. It feels as if you're almost a little stuffy, so in order to break up the mucus and rid it from my lungs, I have to do treatments. For me, I don't know anything different than living with CF. Throughout my life, though, I've always been active. I'm a huge runner, I've been a water-skier since I was four, a basketball player since I was eight, a skier since I was fifteen, and I love to jet-ski. Sports-wise, pretty much you name it, I've played it.

CF didn't really change my life growing up, and now it's a matter of monitoring my lung function. Twice a year I measure to see what the lung function is and where the mucus level is. Each day, I also do a treatment, and then three times a day I take an inhaled antibiotic, and I take an antibiotic three times a week, along with a medication every other month to treat my lungs.

Over the years, with my CF, I didn't really know otherwise, but things are okay; it's the diabetes that is a pain, but the CF I can manage. I do have to take insulin, and even though my pancreas still produces insulin, it can't always get through the thick layer of mucus, so the need is for that external insulin. Every so often, my natural insulin makes its way through, but that's when my blood sugar takes a dive, so I never go anywhere without my sugar pills. Sometimes my mouth gets dry, I have a numb feeling, and I may feel tired and weak due to my diabetes, but I have not made any real lifestyle changes.

I probably wouldn't be here without all the treatments I do; I don't have a choice with this progressive disease. I do the treatments because they keep me around. CF will change, and my lungs will get worse as I get older because it is progressive, but I have done a lot of research over the years. I know a lot about CF, like how, in Caucasians, one out of ten people are carriers, and you have to have all the recessive genes to get the disease. Also, although my children carry the gene, they will not get CF because my husband is not a carrier.

Others need to stay positive and do what they need to do. It is said that the life expectancy of people with CF is thirty-seven years old, but I'm thirty-seven now, and it's fine, and I'm not worried, either. I keep doing what I need to do, and I know there are people in their sixties and seventies who are alive and well with CF. Overall I feel great, so now mine is a future of work, play, and teaching my children sports.

CHAPTER 8

Dementia

Linda Bear's Husband

THERE IS A SAYING: *For better or for worse.* When your better half starts to change and is diagnosed with something you cannot change, that is when that age-old adage really rings true.

For my wife, it was little changes at first that we, her family and friends, noticed. She was losing items, such as her passport on our trip to Florence, Italy. Then her hearing caused her to wear hearing aids, and her short-term memory declined, until finally she was diagnosed with dementia.

I remember the signs, with one later trip in particular: the vacation with all twenty kids and grandkids to Santa Margherita, Italy. Linda would lose something and then have to orient herself to get back to where she was before. Those moments stand out vividly in my head. But it was not until in 2010, when my son decided she needed to go to a geriatric center to get checked out that she was officially diagnosed.

With the help of the medication Aricept, which the doctor prescribed, so far she has not gotten lost, and it helps her to not be as forgetful. It also does not hurt that every day Linda has a routine; a pattern of sorts. She gets up every morning to read the paper and then goes on to feed breakfast to our Labrador, Luke, and the new puppy, Bud. I prefer to talk politics and finance while Linda fills me in on golf and her joyous animals. Afterward, Linda goes to our business office with the dogs in tow. The dogs enjoy their stay in the office while she heads to the post office for mail and then other work. Sorting out the mail, lunch, and then back to the office to grab the dogs before heading back home for the night, follows. After work, Linda typically enjoys a walk around a park before we go out for dinner, usually somewhere local. We eat at the same eight restaurants, a sort of pattern in its own right. After dinner, we like to take in a movie before heading home. Following that, it is a little bit of television for me, while Linda reads before a nine or ten p.m. bedtime, which is Luke's cue to hop up on the bed not too shortly after.

On the weekends, we like to play nine holes of golf, which leaves just enough time for dinner after, for us and the dogs. The patterns, routines, and most importantly, the animals, give Linda renewed purpose in life. It is a way to reinvent those previous times she has been through, and most importantly, it makes her happy. We even saw an old friend recently who claimed she was surprised at how well Linda was holding up.

There is a part of this I cannot explain, because as husband and wife, there are things that you just sort of do intuitively; you are not sure what it is, or why it is. However, if you love someone, you do things that you would want done if you were experiencing this.

Today, Linda has all her kids and grandkids around her, both at work in the high-technology business we have, and in her free time. Yes, life used to be different, but a lot of the previous Linda is still there: she never speaks unkindly of anyone, and nothing can rattle her. She is still the wonderful, loving wife I've always had.

CHAPTER 9

Epilepsy

Billy Bear

WHAT A WONDERFUL THING IT is to be able to say that it has now been six to seven years since I have had a seizure. It's a blessing.

When I was fifteen years old visiting Hart, Michigan, I took up horseback riding with a friend. Unluckily, I fell off the horse, landing on my head, which left me unconscious for several minutes. My friend couldn't find me because I fell in a cornfield, but after about ten minutes, I regained consciousness, stood up, and walked home. Needless to say, I was not getting back on the horse. I also never went to the hospital that fateful day.

Three years later, when I was eighteen, I experienced my first seizure. I woke up thinking, *Now I am abnormal.* All these thoughts raced through my head, because I was young and still building my life. I thought, *Who is going to want to be with me now? Who's going to want to marry me and have children?* I was fearful and afraid of what lay ahead for me.

At that time, I was thinking more negatively about life. *Why did this have to happen to me?* I thought, but my brother–in–law told me I was as normal as the rest of them. Somehow that was comforting.

I quickly realized I was going to have trouble getting my driver's license, and I didn't know yet that I was not able to drink alcohol. I went to a neurosurgeon, where I was put on various medications with the diagnosis of epilepsy. I will always have this, and I believe the cause was the brain injury from that horse incident. However, since that fateful day, I have been able to obtain a driver's license (a must so I could get to and from work to earn a living), I have raised a family, and I quit drinking because I discovered alcohol was a cause of seizures.

Unfortunately, I have had a few seizures while driving, which had a set of ramifications that came along with that, but now I can tell if one is coming on. Now my seizures are manageable, and I take my Dilantin. I did have difficulty, but now things are better, as long as I am aware and take care of myself. I am fortunate, because even though I have this problem, if I do things right and handle the treatment properly, it's manageable.

There was a time I went through difficulty controlling epilepsy, but now they can test to make sure I am receiving the proper amount of medication to maintain my seizure-free life. I wish I would have known certain things earlier on, such as which medications work for me and that I should not be drinking. Today, though, I continue to follow the doctor's orders. I no longer drink alcohol, I get plenty of rest, I get my blood tested for the therapeutic level of medicine, and I pray, pray, and then give thanks.

Epilepsy depends on the individual, and the fewer problems you are having, the more reluctant you would be to change, such as with medications. I can say that I would not be alive now without this treatment. This seems scary to people, because not a lot is known about epilepsy, so you need to be sure to take care of yourself.

Now, because of my age, I realize that no one is perfect, and I am much more likely to accept the health problems I have to deal with, as opposed to when I was that eighteen-year-old. My health issues are more normal to me now, whereas when I was eighteen,

I was more afraid of what was happening with my life; there was that fear of the unknown. Epilepsy treatment now is much more advanced. Today, I can say that I am the longest-surviving member of my family, because, unfortunately, everyone else has passed away, but happily, I am still here.

CHAPTER 10

Heart Conditions

Fred Bear's Wife

FRED WAS BORN IN TUPELO, Mississippi, in 1922. His dad, Oscar, was a talented carpenter, but he also farmed in order to take care of his wife, four sons, and two daughters. At that time, the family lived in Tennessee, and making a living was next to impossible. Hoping for a better life, the family moved to Ohio in 1931 in the midst of the Depression.

In the late thirties, the family moved back to Tennessee. During his high-school years in Greenback, Tennessee, Fred worked in the summertime. One summer he got typhoid fever, which set him back a year in school. This did not stop him, and after graduation, he attended Maryville College in Tennessee. It was there that he met his future wife, Thelma Louise Richardson.

World War II intervened, and Fred served in the army engineers in England, France, and the Philippines.

After the war, life was good. Fred and Thelma were married, he graduated from the University of Tennessee, and eventually ended up in Ypsilanti, Michigan, at Eastern Michigan University (EMU) as an admissions counselor. Two children, years of work at EMU, and then retirement followed. Happy years for all.

Fred never smoked cigarettes, but he smoked cigars for many years. During the early eighties, while in New York City on a family vacation, his daughter noticed he was having trouble walking distances, something everyone has to do in NYC. She called and got a doctor's appointment when they returned to Ypsilanti. Fred was diagnosed with blocked arteries and surgery was performed at St. Joseph Hospital in Ypsilanti. At this point, his life changed. He struggled with recovery for many weeks and slept downstairs on a low cot, hugging his pillow. Finally he was able to take hold, and so he changed his diet to not eat red meat, use olive oil instead of Crisco, and eat no fried foods. He also quit the cigar habit. He started walking every day, and this became his salvation. He walked for miles and started losing weight. He would continue to have a daily vodka martini too. Cooking food to keep healthy was his new passion.

The lesson is to take control. Fred lived almost twenty years longer and was always a bright light in his family's life.

At the end, his heart would not pump properly and congestive heart failure was the final blow. His change in life habits allowed him to live longer, benefit from the sunshine of Florida, and have a lasting, loving relationship with his grandchildren. All to his family's joy.

Jim Bear

The symptoms that came on before my quadruple bypass surgery were not really anything; rather, it was a surgery that revealed the problem when I had an angioplasty procedure. You see, what I mean is, after a routine check-up, it was discovered that the bottom of my heart was not getting blood.

From there, everything happened pretty quickly. Basically, I went in right away to have my quadruple-bypass surgery. The way it was done, which is pretty typical for this type of surgery, was to use the arteries from my leg to create a new passage for blood flow to my heart that was lacking and not functioning properly. I was told this was a common way to do this procedure.

This surgery was done recently, and it turns out—simply put—things have been good ever since. Sometimes I do, however, have shortness of breath, but that too will get better with time. My regimen, which comes from doctor's orders, is to take my medication and do more walking.

My story may be brief and sound simple to some, but I can honestly say now that without this treatment, I would have been dead within a couple years. And no, I cannot say my lifestyle was really any different before I had this surgery.

If I had some words of wisdom or advice to you others (as I sit here as a sixty-eight-year-old bypass surgery survivor), I would say the surgery was a reasonable procedure, and actually, it only took me a couple of days to recuperate. I would most certainly recommend this surgery for people in my situation going through what I have gone through.

Mike Bear

In 2001, I collapsed on the golf course, but at the time I was only diagnosed with atrial flutter, a condition where the heart rate is too rapid. Ultimately, after days in the hospital and different blood tests taken, I had an ablation performed, but there were no typical signs or symptoms that led to my soon-to-be double bypass surgery.

Historically, I had high cholesterol, which I took Lipitor for, but in 2009 (eight years after my initial collapse), I felt something again as an avid golfer on the course: shortness of breath. This led to a follow-up, where a 99 percent blockage in one area of my heart and a 97 percent blockage in another were found; however, stents were not a viable option for me, so the only one left was bypass surgery.

In June 2009, I went to see Dr. Andrew Pruitt of Michigan Heart to have my surgery performed. The first day after in intensive care was the most difficult—so difficult that while on all the medications,

I was so out of it that I tried to pull the tube out of my throat. Although the surgery went as well as expected, by the second day, there was a dicey situation that brought on a reoccurrence of my rapid heart rate.

It also turns out that Michigan Heart has a great program for recovery, equipped with videos and booklets of exercises. The hospital stay went well. I was told it would be a four-day experience, which left me quite tired after the surgery, and I gradually felt better as the days passed, continuing to walk and build my endurance. Within four weeks post surgery, I was driving again, and seven weeks later, I was back playing golf.

Obviously, golf is a big part of my life, but it was also a big part of my health. That, along with walking and changing my eating habits to include only a little red meat, no butter, cream, or ice cream, and more fruits and vegetables, all contributed. My lifestyle was not significantly different before my surgery, but the changes of exercise and diet were not too bad to change, either. It is all working pretty well, and I feel pretty good now at age sixty-one.

I think if it was not for this double bypass, I would be dead or significantly restricted in what I could do. I would be worried that if I overexerted myself, I could cause a heart attack. One positive is that I have never had a heart attack; I beat that before it could happen, and I was lucky I did not have one on the golf course.

I think you have to talk to others who have had a similar surgery and get to know the surgeons before you make a decision. I had a good feeling about Dr. Pruitt, and practically speaking, I knew the surgery was the best option for me. Make sure to get a second opinion, or at the very least, get some advice. Ultimately, this was my only choice.

❧

Al Smithson

If I only had to name one constant in my life of seventy-five years, it would be that I have worked hard and always will. That is something that has not changed in the eight years since my triple-bypass heart surgery.

It all started when I had a stress test done, and a blockage was found in my heart, but I am happy to say now that I am doing well ever since that surgery.

I'll bet at this point you may be wondering what my secret is. Well, it consists of a combination of things: exercise, walking, vitamins, and eating healthy. Today, I still cut the eight acres of grass at my home and work on the yard, I still do a lot of walking every day, and of course, I try to eat healthy by watching what I eat (even if that means I cannot eat a lot of fried food).

After my triple bypass, the doctor initially gave me exercises to perform during rehab; however, following that regimen, it was up to me to change my lifestyle (I knew I had to a little bit), so I started with eating habits and exercising. I think it is helping now because I enjoy what I am doing, and most importantly, I feel better.

Call it my Southern upbringing (I'm from Tennessee), but you cannot just sit in the house. Like I said before, I have always worked hard, and always will, so if you are in a situation like mine, go and get the operation done; please do not wait. And when you are done with that operation, make sure to exercise regularly, eat nourishing food, and avoid food that is unhealthy (like junk food).

Before my bypass, I was working and still do; anything I want to do, I do. Mostly, it does not tire me out, and I still feel all right. When I am not working hard at home, I enjoy traveling and escaping off to Florida, where I can walk along the beaches.

All I can say is that the way I do things, I feel okay, even after all these years. To be honest, even after the surgery, I was up and out of that hospital bed and was walking around fairly quickly. Although the doctors frowned upon my walking around so soon (you know, because of hospital's and doctor's orders), I felt well enough to do so. The best advice I can give is to catch these types of incidents, incidents like mine, before you have a heart attack.

But this is my story: the blockage was found, the operation was done, and now I continue to live a healthy lifestyle.

Daryle Bear

I never thought at age sixty-seven that I would be sitting here in the South Lyon, Michigan, area telling about a quadruple bypass, because the truth is, I never even noticed anything wrong. I had no symptoms that I recognized; sure I was a little tired, but really, when I went in for the tests, it was because my wife told me it was the right thing to do, to get a check-up. It turns out, after several tests, including a stress test, that the doctors found a spot on my heart. I was sent to a heart specialist, who performed an electrocardiography (EKG) to measure the activity of my heart, which was discovered to be in atrial fibrillation (AF or A-Fib), or beating 140 beats per minute. This was January 2010, but the strange part was, I did not feel my chest pounding.

My wife and I canceled our trip to Florida because the doctors flat out told me *I was not going to make it*. Now can you imagine that? Hearing that news? Neither could I, but I knew I needed to check into the hospital, so I admitted myself into emergency for surgery.

For my situation, heart problems seem to be hereditary. My mother had a heart attack and bypass surgery in her early sixties, and my brother also had a heart attack and bypass surgery. But the mind-boggling part for me was that I had never had high blood pressure or a heart attack. I was upset. Upset because I thought, *Why is this happening to me? It shouldn't happen, I did everything right.* But the truth is, you cannot escape your family history, and you cannot beat genetics.

After the initial surprise and anger passed, I was glad I'd had the operation done. After the discovery of four blockages, the heart bypass was performed, and one week later, I was back in the comfort of my own home. During that time, however, I was told to watch what I ate and monitor my sugar intake. It also turned out I came out of the hospital with type 2 diabetes. It is hard for me to distinguish whether or not it was caused by a shock to my system.

Today, I take medication for my diabetes, but I no longer have a rapid heartbeat. I know how to take my pulse properly, and I stay healthy by paying attention to my body. Eating is done in moderation, salt has been cut back, and I stay active with games of golf. Little by little, I am getting into the swing of things by pacing myself, which is hard for an impatient person like me.

Luckily, I have not had to make any drastic lifestyle changes. I still work hard in my job at a golf course, and actually, I believe my workload has increased since my operation. I enjoy keeping busy, remaining active, and mostly not sitting around feeling sorry for myself. The doctors told me I can do virtually anything, but I try to do it at a minimal pace, even if that is not typical of my personality. Yes, I get tired from time to time, but as a creature of habit, I will remain active.

At first I experienced surprise and bitterness, but I am truly thankful this condition was discovered. I also went through the rehab that was offered to me and found I am not the only guy on the block who went through this. It means a lot to be able to relate to others, and it helps to know people who went through a similar situation. I have learned to accept what has happened, even when I thought it should not have. Nevertheless, if not for this treatment, I would probably be in a pine box. I can definitely say that.

I am sixty-seven years old, and that does not mean I am old, and positivity is what helped make circumstance better. I have to watch myself, but things are good in my heart now.

If it was not for my wife being adamant about a stress test, I would not have known anything was wrong. So if someone tells you to do something, as in my case, do it, do not wait. Be serious about life and yourself and pay attention to your own body. My wife is thankful, and now, as I look back on it all, I am too.

❦

Bill Lane

At age eighty, I still fix things around the house and go down to Mike's store in South Lyon, Michigan, to see my buddies. I'm not a complicated guy. I've been married for sixty-one years, and my kids, all in there sixties, live within a fifty-mile radius in Michigan.

My doctor sent me to the University of Michigan Hospital for a check-up, and there they decided to use medication to treat my condition first. Soon after though, my personal doctor said it was an emergency, and they put stents in and performed a quadruple bypass.

Before I had surgery, I would go for a walk and only get so far before my whole body would just stop. After surgery, and up until now, I have walked more than four-hundred miles.

You're probably not interested in this, but I married my wife sixty-one years ago, and I met her because the fellow I worked with at the lumber mill was her dad. He asked me if I would give her a ride to work because she worked in a five-and-dime store fifty miles away. He gave me two dollars a week for gas. This was during my time in Berkley, West Virginia. One day, some of my friends asked if I would like to go swimming, and if I had a girlfriend I could bring along. I decided to ask my boss's daughter if she wanted to go. Her response was that she did not want to be seen in a bathing suit with people she did not know. We were married three months later.

Back to Michigan and my bypass. I told the doctors I didn't have time for an operation because I had to go back to West Virginia to winterize my house. My son said he would take care of the house.

I had the bypass done, and then we went to our house in West Virginia, and I fixed most of the food. I had turkey dinner on Thanksgiving, just like I wanted to do. That was five years ago. The boys at Mike's store think I'm going to make it another sixteen years, but I don't know.

Look, I'm just a hardworking American who came to Michigan and worked in the car assembly-line business. I started at Chrysler and finished up with Ford's—that's what we old-timers call Ford Motor Company. In fact, I've been retired for twenty-one years.

The only reason I'm doing this story is to help someone else who gets scared about bypass surgery. I would like him or her to know that the guys at University of Michigan Hospital are pretty good.

Hank Bear

There was nothing I couldn't do before I had this operation.

Although I didn't know it at the time, the first warning sign was when I had a transient ischemic attack (TIA) or a "warning stroke." I was born with a defect in my heart, but that was something I did not know, either, until age sixty-eight. During this mini-stroke, I remember feeling numb and being unable to talk. I was rushed to the hospital, but they couldn't find anything wrong with me. Just prior to this incident, I had a fractured foot, so as a last resort, they took a look at my heart, and that's when they discovered the hole. I had never had any heart problems in the past, so the doctors determined I had a blood clot in my fractured foot that had traveled up to my heart, jumped chambers, and traveled to my brain, causing the TIA. As a son who experienced his own mother dying in his arms from a stroke, this was a scary experience.

That was the start of it all.

From there I went to a specialist, who gave me two choices: either live the rest of my life on Coumadin (Warfarin), or get the hole in my heart repaired. I also asked my family doctor his opinion, and he advised me not to get the heart repair but to take Coumadin. However, I did further research and discovered that the medication is not 100 percent effective in preventing blood clots and declines in effectiveness over the years. That's why I decided to have the atrial septal defect (ASD) repair.

In order to sew the hole in my heart, my chest bone had to be cracked, but what I had not been told was that when they crack open your chest, you lose approximately 30 percent of your flexibility, which results in losing 30 percent of your ability to breathe. No one I consulted with ever mentioned this procedure would cause this.

When your lungs can't expand or contract fully and work at a decreased level, they make your heart work harder to make up for this decline. This is the worst thing they could have done to me, because over time, your heart is affected by having to work so hard to make up for the decline in the ability of the lungs.

Soon after, I was experiencing shortness of breath. When I complained to the doctors, they kept blaming my years of smoking, even though I had quit smoking fifteen years ago. Soon after that, I contracted a bad case of bronchitis, which due to the decreased ability of my lungs quickly turned into pneumonia. It wasn't long afterward that I was diagnosed with chronic obstructive pulmonary disorder (COPD) and congestive heart failure (CHF). I was in trouble all right. I was placed on oxygen on a daily basis, on more medication than I would have ever believed, and my heart continued to work too hard and went into atrial fibrillation. I checked my pulse daily, and felt my pulse beating slowly at times and very rapidly at other times. Again, I was placed on even more medication and was in and out of the hospital each month for a year because of this problem. I knew I had to lose some weight so my heart and lungs did not have to work so hard, but I couldn't walk very far or exercise because I wasn't breathing very well.

One day, while in my internist's office, I was told to go to the emergency room right away because I needed to have a pacemaker installed immediately. When I entered, the doctor on staff examined me and said I did not need a pacemaker but felt I was being overmedicated. They kept me in the hospital for three days, took me off the heart medications, and within two days, I was able to walk down the halls of the hospital, something I had not been able to do for a year. My heart rhythm went almost back to normal and only an occasional arrhythmia could be detected in the EKG.

Once home, I kept exercising and remained on a strict diet of fruits, no fat, veggies, occasional meat, and no bread. Today, I still follow this diet.

It has taken me a year to get to where I am today. I only need a nebulizer (an inhaler for emergencies), and I also carry an oxygen tank with me. I can't do as much as I used to, but I can walk a little further now.

If I hadn't had my chest cracked, I wouldn't have COPD or CHF. The procedures might have changed, but if I were to do it again, I would never let them open my chest cavity. You have to get a couple of opinions, which I thought I had, but I feel I should have researched on my own even further.

I know how to work around my condition now, even though I may not like the limitations this places on me, but at least I am living. Maintain yourself and have a good attitude; that's my advice. I think I am younger than seventy-seven. You can't lie down and die. If you feel you are going to die, that's when you need to live more.

❦

Ed Bear

Men have to understand they are not invincible. Even being a former college athlete, like me, does not mean you are Superman. I found this to be true.

In May 2003, I went to get a physical and within the same month, my sister, who was living alone with her thirty-year-old daughter who has Down Syndrome, was diagnosed with lung cancer. My sister passed away the following month, leaving her daughter behind with the matter of legal guardian to worry about. Fortunately, I have a wonderful daughter who became the legal guardian of my niece.

Between family and work (which was going horribly), I was completely stressed out and headed to the gym to relieve some of the stress and anxiety. I rode the bike for ten miles, walked the treadmill for two miles, and then lifted weights. However, by the time I got to the weights, I had a strange feeling. I thought it was just a pulled muscle, but as my jaw cramped up, I knew I was having a heart attack. Although, being a man, I did not tell anyone (no one ever said we men are smart) and instead drove myself to Providence Hospital in Michigan. During this time I was experiencing shortness of breath, so by the time I reached the hospital, I was having a heart attack at age fifty-seven.

After the angioplasty, the doctors put two stents in the left anterior descending (LAD), known as the "widow maker." Two days later, I was sent home, only to develop a blood clot quickly after, which meant a second angioplasty since I was on the verge of another heart attack.

A well-known fact, or rather problem, is that following a heart attack, men also experience depression. It turned out I was suffering from and was diagnosed with acute depression, and you either get it under control, or you die; that's what I was told. That is a harsh statement to hear, but men need to realize depression can cause cardiovascular problems and can kill you. Trust me, I've had days that were so bad I could not even get out of bed.

But I am here, seven years later, with a clean bill of health. Now at sixty-four, my cholesterol looks good and the doctors seem happy with my results. I say do what the doctors tell you to do. My advice to men is to not be such macho jerks, get help, realize your shortcomings, and do what the doctors tell you. I am probably healthier now cardiovascular-wise than I was seven years ago.

There is no question that I would be dead right now without the treatments. If I had not followed the doctor's advice and then started to eat better (things like more fish and salads), I would not be here. You go from feeling like you are invincible to realizing you are mortal. But remember, stress is a horrible thing and a potential killer, and you have to work to keep it to a minimum whenever possible.

My lifestyle was different before the surgery; there were times I was on the job more than one hundred nights a year, and that is stressful. I am retired now, but jobs can create stress, family can cause stress, but the key is to remember that stress can kill you.

Today I feel terrific cardiovascular health-wise. Sure there are some bumps and bruises along the way, but this is the cleanest bill of health I have had in years. So take your medicine, watch what you do, and get rid of stress.

❦

Paul Schenk

My daughters would tell you that I live life like I am a sixteen-year-old, even though I am seventy-three. I push the limits, but that is because I like to live my life to the fullest, and I never want to slow down. That is one of my faults in life.

At age forty-three, things changed a bit, and I was forced to slow down my life in Kaleva, Michigan, when I was diagnosed with chronic obstructive pulmonary disease (COPD) and congestive heart failure. Basically, my heart was so weak that it could not pump the fluid, which is part of the lung disorder that makes it hard to breath. Yes, I was also a smoker for years, but after this news, I quit cold turkey. To add to this, however, I always had a love of the outdoors that included nights around the campfire, but breathing in those toxic fumes and burning wood did not help the matter.

My daughters would also tell you I can be a pretty stubborn man because I liked to believe I would live forever. I did take my doctor's orders and started on a series of steroids, inhalers, breathing treatments, and experimental medications. Some of these made me ill while most worked well on the shortness of breath. I also stopped building the campfires I loved so much.

In 1998, I was diagnosed with congestive heart failure, which led to receiving a pacemaker in my chest. That pacemaker was soon changed to a defibrillator pacemaker, with yet another new pacemaker following. My diet also changed, meaning salt-free foods, no alcohol, and watching my sugar intake, thanks to my wife, Debbie, who always tried to create new sugar-free desserts. As for exercise, well, some may say I get too much. From sunup to sundown, I enjoy working in the yard, but it too became a strain on my ticker.

But if I have one message to tell all of you, it is, plain and simple, that the doctors do not have all the answers. Unfortunately, with them it can be a numbers game, which boils down to making money. That is why everyone needs an advocate.

I am not going to lie; the pacemaker saved my life and got me through the days where I would black out from my illness. It gave me many more wonderful years with my family and friends, and I could have passed away ten years earlier if not for that tiny machine.

The doctors first told me I was not going to make it through the night, but in my mind, they were wrong (and of course they were).

In fact, I was told several times I was not going to live as long as I did, but the truth is, I was not going to let them bring me down.

Doctors only know so much. Sure they practice medicine, but they also are equipped to make educated guesses, which means even doctors can be wrong from time to time. That meant it was up to me to do the best I could to find what works best for my body. I had the support around me and fought hard to stay alive and healthy. Even with a heart that only functions at 20 percent, and having to rely on an oxygen tank, my willpower came into play. For me, it was my positive attitude, and that is something the doctors could not give or prescribe to me.

My positivity helped me get up in the morning, kept the days going, and kept me strong. I also entered holistic foods into my diet, ate fewer processed foods, and increased my vitamin intake. I believe this is what has helped me live longer.

I know my body started to slow down, even if my sharp mind hasn't. I will always have a love of hunting and speed-racing hobbies, but my body just cannot keep up. It is hard to be in a body that cannot keep up with the mind; it can be exhausting. That is why I like to live every day like it is my last: hard, fast, and furious, to get the most out of each day. Heck, I do not even like sleeping all that much because I want to get in a full day.

My daughter, Laurie, told me that she admired how, even if I was in miserable pain, I was always in a good mood. She said people see how I am happy, loving, caring, and *all heart*. I guess in the end, positivity really is the best medicine.

Cyrus Bear

I was always concerned with trying to keep the pounds down, but as I got older, my legs didn't allow me to run like I used to, so I switched to walking. I would walk up to four miles at times, even through the more than eighty-degree weather because I really loved it.

It wasn't until ten years ago, when I was in Orlando, Florida, for business and decided to leave my motel room at about 9:30 a.m. for a walk, when about half a mile later, I started to feel chest pressure. It was unlike anything I had ever felt before. Having gone through coronary artery disease with both my parents, I was not an unsuspecting victim of chest pain. Immediately, I knew I was experiencing angina, which is typically caused by an artery that is blocked or partially blocked.

At this point, fifteen hundred miles from home, all I could think was that I didn't want my chest to be cracked open for bypass surgery. That was when I turned around, and decided to stroll back to my motel to instantly take two aspirin. The pressure and pain went away rather quickly before I got back though so I still didn't know what to do next. Instead of the smart thing, going to the hospital, I relaxed the pressure with aspirin and went about the rest of my day.

This same situation happened for about three days, and one day, I even drove to the emergency hospital just to sit in the car. I never went through the doors. Through it all, however, I kept walking to keep the blood flowing, all while living on aspirin and God's watchful and protecting hand.

In the meantime, I called my wife, who contacted our general practitioner (who is also a noted cardiologist) to set up an appointment for when I got home. That following Friday, I explained to my doctor what I had been through, and he was wise and suggested going to a pain clinic for the emergency. It turned out, forty-eight hours later, in April 2000, I had a stent placed in my right coronary artery that happened to be about 80 percent closed.

I quickly went back to walking even more diligently than ever, hoping to keep my arteries clear. Unfortunately, three months later, the chest pain came back. The stent had scarred over, but they cleared it up, and here I am today at age sixty-five without any problems.

There is no question that without the stent I would be dead because of a clogged artery. But what I feel is keeping me clear, other than my medication, is walking. I have been walking year-round outside, anywhere from three to five days a week, for about thirty to forty-five minutes. Walking has been instrumental to keeping things on the straight and narrow, and without it, I would probably not have been able to maintain the health I have.

All in all, get out and walk, listen to your doctor, and drink lots of red wine. I do. Keep walking and help keep those arteries clear.

❦

Pete Niedzielski

If I did not have bypass surgery when I did, I would have had a massive heart attack and would be gone by now, plain and simple; that was nineteen years ago.

My symptoms were not of the heart but rather a pulled muscle. In August 1991, I was installing a hot tub I had made with railroad tire parts, and the morning after, I woke up with a sore shoulder. Figuring it was from moving the tires, I ignored the pain for a few days, but when it did not get better, I decided to go to the chiropractor. However, he told me there was nothing he could do because it was a muscle problem and suggested I go see my doctor.

When I walked into my doctor's office, he looked at me, asked what was wrong, and I told him about my shoulder. To my surprise, he said not to worry about it, but he wanted to perform an EKG. When I asked him why, he said I just did not look right. Now if anyone else would have said that to me, I probably would have told them I did not like the way they looked either. It turns out the EKG was fine, but I still wanted to know about my shoulder. His answer was to schedule a stress test.

After a positive result from the stress test, three weeks passed, and a turn of events led me to the hospital for a heart catheterization. I was told I would need a stent. I must say it is quite unnerving to hear your cardiologist say, "I don't like this" and then tell you you are a candidate for bypass surgery. The following Monday I had my quadruple bypass on five blocked arteries.

Afterward, one of the first things I remember the doctor telling me was that I needed to get more exercise or I would be back for more surgery in a few years. Even worse, there was the possibility of a heart attack. Walking, he said, is the best exercise there is, and by the time I was due back in eight weeks to see my doctor, I was to report back to him about how I was walking at least one mile a day.

The day I got back from the hospital, I decided exercise was the best dose of medicine for me, as opposed to more surgery or a possible heart attack. I walked two tenths of a mile, which was the distance from my house to my mailbox and back. And then each day it went on, and I walked a little further than the next, until about four weeks later, I was walking a mile in about twenty minutes. I decided if I could do a mile, I could do two miles and so forth, until my next eight week check-up. It just so happens I was doing two miles in forty-two minutes.

Following that, about two and a half months after my surgery, my wife informed me about an indoor walking club at one of the nearby South Lyon, Michigan, schools that took place during the winter months. I joined the club and challenged myself to see how many miles I could go and how fast I could walk those miles. By the end of the club season, five months later, I was walking four miles in one hour.

Now, at age seventy-one, and nineteen years after my surgery, I still walk inside with the club during the winter months and outside during the summer months (although maybe not as much in the summer as I should). I really look forward to the start of the walking club each September, and frankly, this is the only exercise I have ever been able to stick with for more than a couple months. I also continue to take my blood and cholesterol medications to keep my arteries clean and to stay healthy. I walk five miles in sixty-five minutes, five days a week, and I have not had any more surgeries or a heart attack since. The best news is that my doctor tells me I am in great health.

Before, I did not worry about things and did not pay as much attention to exercise, although I always did a lot of physical work on the outside of the house. However, according to the doctors, you need to do cardio exercise too, to remain in good health.

It was pure luck on my part that I found out about my heart when I did, but listen to your doctor—one you can trust.

℀

Duke Bear

The onset of symptoms started in early 2006 when I started to experience episodes of what one would describe as "room spins" or "room tilt" (vertigo). In my case, this was due to a partial blockage in the basilar artery in my brainstem. I know, it's a bit of a scary condition, because you can be sitting or standing and then all of a sudden the room will start to spin or tilt.

That following January, my bad cholesterol climbed, and was not good, taking into account the normal ranges. Up until this point, I was being treated for high cholesterol, but after a magnetic resonance angiogram (MRA) was performed, it was revealed that I had 50 percent heart blockage. At fifty-one years old, my neurologist started me on the statin drug Zocor (simvastatin) to lower my cholesterol.

A blocked artery can be a critical condition, and if not treated can lead to a stroke. I had a few small ones known as transient ischemic attacks (TIA). A year later, I requested another MRA to determine whether the blockage in my artery had lessened, and to my relief, there was considerable improvement.

Later that year, I was laid off from my job, but I continued to exercise. After a while, however, the reality of being out of work took its toll and sent me into a depression. Although I was exercising three to four days per week, I was still becoming a couch potato and indulging in junk food. I did, however, continue to run, but later that spring I was on the treadmill, and I gradually started to feel a tightening on my left side and weakness in my arm, which would spread to the center of my chest.

About three months later, after my annual physical, I was told my cholesterol was good, but I needed a stress test and angiogram for the chest pains. The results were not so good, and the cardiologist said all four major arteries were 90 to 95 percent blocked. I then had bypass surgery, which turned out to be, in total, a three-vessel bypass with cardio rehab to follow in the next four months, which went very well with no problems.

After a procedure like this, one does not have the same energy and stamina, and the effects from the medication started to become evident. Over time, I could not sleep for nights on end, suffered from panic attacks, lost weight, had memory loss, became weak, and my bowel habits changed. But then I stumbled across a cholesterol book I heard about over the radio and was so overwhelmed by the relevance to my condition, I ordered it right away. Through this I learned a lot about medications, how they affect your body and mind, and about nutraceuticals and vitamins.

People have to realize that high LDL ("bad") cholesterol is a symptom, not the cause, and cholesterol helps prevent brain loss and cancer, aids digestion, and detoxifies the body against depression and aging. The book also outlined medical websites, as well as the connection between depression, memory loss, muscle weakness, insomnia, and other symptoms; all of which I was experiencing.

I also went to see a homeopath who helped me formulate the protocol I am currently taking. Before, I used to take four medications to treat my high cholesterol, but now I take nutraceuticals and vitamins, and it's well worth it. Now I feel much better and have the peace of mind knowing what I am doing is safe and has no side effects. It is extremely important to remember that it's not just a matter of changing what you take but a life change that involves proper diet and exercise. Now I exercise five days a week, and my cholesterol is within the normal range.

My message to pass on to others is to really seek a knowledgeable cardiologist who leans toward homeopathic remedies. Most importantly, research your medical condition and don't necessarily believe everything your doctor tells you. Thoroughly research the medications and the drug industry and find out for yourself what the real intent is. I hope this benefits other people with a similar health condition.

William Zilke

First, let me say one thing; without humor, faith in something higher, and the support of my friends and family, the healing process can be slow and difficult. I chose humor, although there is nothing funny about my aortic aneurysm, or the medical and psychological conditions that led up to it.

I was born in 1957 to a traditional yet extremely conservative family of the period, which also included a violent, alcoholic father who would have made Senator Joe McCarthy look like Jerry Garcia. My dad earned minimum wage while my mom raised us kids. As poor as we were, he still maintained a "No wife of mine will work, have opinions, wear pants, or have friends" attitude. She was allowed, however, "to do the painting, wash clothes with a wringer washer, and speak when I need to bounce drunken babble off someone." That's the way I saw things growing up.

My father, who was fifteen years older than my mother, was also raised by Victorians where children were *seen* and not *heard*. As a jazz musician on the weekends, he was also a physically and emotionally abusive drunk. I tell you this because it ties into my health. Unfortunately, I was not born healthy; I needed blood transfusions before age one, which probably made me a financial burden, and since I only had an older sister at the time, the target of his violent rage happened to become me. Elbowing a toddler or shoving him out of his way was the *norm*. One time my dad was so drunk, he even threw me—three years old at the time—into the fireplace, which was mercifully unlit.

At age four I contracted scarlet fever, which can cause a lot of damage to the internal organs, stunting the growth and output capacity. My father wouldn't allow me to be taken to the hospital, much due to the fact it was an inconvenience to his time, as it was to his overbearing mother (we lived in her house), who also refused to let my mother take me to the hospital. Why, I couldn't tell you. In those days, in that neighborhood of Detroit's northwest side, having drunken fathers who beat their kids or wives was not that unusual. I even recall that my first artwork, put up on the refrigerator, was eerily similar to Munch's *The Scream*. There were no school programs or counselors to turn to then, and if you did, juvenile hall was as likely an option as a foster home. But all the while, this stressed my already weakened heart.

Most of my friends had not known any other life other than a stumbling, violent father, many of whom were untreated, post-traumatic stress victims from World War II and the Korean conflict. I am, of course, talking about my closest friends' fathers, not all combat veterans, but this meant you could get hit for no real reason other than being in arm's length of a dangerous, drunken father. One of my earliest memories is being chased while screaming and hiding under the piano where he couldn't reach me. At this point, the stress on the heart must have been dangerous beyond bounds. I had no idea I was born with a defective heart, so the sheer terror of running and hiding under the piano to escape another broken nose sent my heart into overdrive with adrenaline.

Many medical issues, even in 1964, could have been diagnosed if you had a father who could afford health care. A child's health care fell into my dad's definition of "women's work," sort of like plugging up a broken nose or shoveling snow. However, growing up in a working-class Detroit neighborhood, with a rapidly rising crime rate with escalating street violence, forced me to toughen up in my early years, where I went to "the school of hard knocks." This meant a daily pounding on my aortic valve, millimeter by millimeter.

My defective heart strengthened over the days by walking more than three miles to Cody High School in Michigan, since we could only afford bus fare one way. I was also very active in baseball and football, and nothing, except getting winded pretty easily for someone my age, suggested my heart was a ticking time-bomb. When I was sixteen, like most guys my age with abusive fathers who lived in a rundown neighborhood with no real possibility of finding a job, I took the flight out of Detroit and enlisted in the US Coast Guard. So the day I turned seventeen, I left. My blood pressure was actually on the low side back then, and I never suspected any lurking, serious health issues, let alone a potentially fatal aneurysm. In 1975, I got my honorable discharge when funding for extra troops for the Vietnam War ended, and after that, I became my own worst enemy.

I sang in what was then the burgeoning punk/alternative music scene where alcohol was plentiful; nonstop partying was a way of life, and I smoked cigarettes. In those days, San Francisco, New York, and Los Angeles held the incubating environment for cutting-edge music and entertainment, and alcohol was everywhere, even at my day job. All the time, every drink and cigarette beat my heart one step closer to literally exploding.

When I moved back to Michigan in 1984, I settled into what turned into an unhappy marriage with a person whose biggest joy in life was to insult me publicly. I was hardly infused with self-esteem, but opposed to most males raised by abusive men who seem to lash out at women and children, I went the other way. I don't argue with women or yell at kids, and I'm proud to say my current wife, Paulette, boasts she's treated like a queen. With my first wife, though, I let it roll off my back and drowned the pain with alcohol.

One evening, I spent several hours at my ex-wife's parents' house, where they burned kerosene for heat. The fumes, which are brutal on your sinuses, made me return home not feeling well and gave me trouble breathing. The next morning, I sneezed once, sneezed again a little heavier, and my nose started bleeding. The alcohol abuse had finally thinned the blood, and it poured wherever it wanted through my weakened heart. At first it came slow, and then it went from light to heavy, pumping blood for about three or four hours. I went to Oakwood Hospital in Belleville, Michigan, but the bleeding had stopped by then. My blood pressure, however, was 180/120.

After several months of not being able to lower my blood pressure through medications, Dr. Mamatha Agrawal, who saved my life, sent me to the University of Michigan. To my surprise, the doctors told me I had an aortic aneurysm that had gone untreated, and I was also born with a heart defect lacking one valve leaflet in the heart, which I didn't find out about until I was forty-one. But that's not even the amazing part of the story.

My nosebleed gave the blood an escape route, rather than filling my lungs and stomach with blood, which would have killed me. The doctors said such things like the nosebleeds do happen, but the odds are very slim; the bleeding is fatal most of the time. Following that, I underwent surgery in October 1998 for aortic repair.

Contrary to most people who want play-by-play details of their surgeries, once they told me they were going to crack open my ribs, take my heart out, and stop it, I told them, "Stop! I don't want to see pictures or videos. I'll show up for surgery and when I wake up, I'll start my life again from there."

However, I had to recuperate alone. I did the housecleaning up to that point, but now I was off my feet and could barely walk to the bathroom without blacking out. The house was getting filthier and filthier, piled with clutter and animal dander and fur due to my ex-wife and her hoarding problem. The living conditions were quickly turning horrid and unhealthy, and living with a hoarder is beyond anything that makes sense; arguing only made my condition worse.

One night the furnace went out (I don't remember for how long), and in early November, it was cold. I would black out from my illness and wake up shivering, face down with a bloody nose on a dirty carpet. Again, I felt like I was *under the piano*. Not knowing how much blood I lost or how long I had been passed out, I only wanted to crawl back to bed and hope I didn't wake up again. This was two weeks after the surgery that I began passing out and being blinded by "haloes," which is a pre-stroke, high blood-pressure condition similar to "seeing stars" or the inability to focus on anything because my vision would "brown out." Haloes are a side effect of some heart medications, and I don't mean the illusion of imagined rings of light around people that some claim to see ("auras"). What I mean is, if you close your eyes, rub them, and your vision is blurred afterward because you can't see anything or get your bearings, this is what I experienced. I was immediately hospitalized again for pre-renal failure.

Due to the condition of my house and the issues with my ex-wife, I no longer had friends, and my parents were too old to help out. Here I was, forty-one and *hiding underneath the piano* again. But in 2001, the very first day I truly felt good after three years, I decided to do something with my new chance at life and help people. I had been a writer, photographer, an artist, and a musician my whole life. Now my life consisted of a verbally abusive mate who tore at my self-esteem at every opportunity. I was alone—married and alone—figure that out. I stopped and took stock of all I had been through and bottomed out emotionally.

I decided I wasn't going to live my life vegetating on a couch, as the doctors warned me my life could become post-aneurysm, and I walked into several newspaper offices and offered to write, draw cartoons, take photos, or do anything for a shot at a writer's job. I was literally laughed at and almost escorted out of a couple of offices because my total writing experience consisted of songs, humor, and reviews for the alternative press; plus, I didn't have a college degree. But I regained my need for creativity, and the long process of getting published by freelancing for magazines wasn't happening fast enough. My entire life, from the coast guard until I met my first wife, had been one of creativity, performance, and independence. It was the era of telling myself "Do it—the most they can say is no. Why not be a singer, writer, or artist if you want?"

Alcohol, smoking, post-traumatic stress, depression, and lack of self-esteem had held me back far enough. I walked into the office of the *Belleville View* (in Michigan), offered my services, and the editor genuinely liked my cartoons and humor. I worked for free for almost two years, and that did my heart a world of good. Belleville and Van Buren Township city halls were all within walking distance, so I walked miles every day and built my heart back up, along with some strong relationships with the residents. It not only raised my confidence but helped strengthen my heart.

Then came September 11, 2001. At that point, the newspaper needed all hands out on the street, and I became an official reporter, as well as a feature writer, not allowing them to know I had a serious heart condition, that I couldn't drive, or was living with a hoarder. I led two lives: the fairly well-liked (I think) town fixture at all events, willing to help anyone in press to give them a voice, yet I couldn't socialize at my own house, which puzzled the people I was closest to.

Now, ten years later, I am remarried to the most wonderful woman I have ever met, still walk my "beat" in town, and take my medication religiously. Due to haloes, random loss of vision, and heart medications that make me dizzy, I don't drive anymore. I realize now that low self-esteem in others is what creates and fosters poor self-image in others, though I do not understand child abuse or humiliating heart patients. I suppose, to sum this up, you have to stay positive and believe in a higher power and kindness to others no matter how hard your life. You have to believe in something because stress and negativity will hurt your heart, literally and figuratively.

If you face a potentially fatal health situation, surround yourself with light. If you're blessed enough to be given a second chance, don't waste it. Life is short, and you're living it with a serious health problem. I hope my story helps anyone who was abused, or has a birth defect or aneurysm. The mind and body are connected, and removing unhappiness and negativity from your life is just as important as taking your medication. In fact, low self-esteem, verbal or physical abuse, and stress will likely counteract the good your prescriptions do.

If you've been given a second chance, don't hide under the piano. Play it.

Bill Bear

I've always had a heart murmur, but when the doctors gave me three choices: restrict my activity, have a heart valve transplant, or die, I think I chose the right one.

I had no symptoms before my transplant, and at the time, I had injured my ankle in a horseback riding accident, which happened to play a role in the discovery of my heart condition. One night I was out on the town, and I stopped to talk to some people I ran into, and in order to catch up with my friends I was with, I started to jog. Although my ankle was injured I started to run a little, to test and see how it felt, but once I started to run harder, I fainted. I was taken to the emergency room, where tests were taken to determine whether my heart had indeed gotten worse. Logically, I didn't have much choice because I didn't want to restrict my activity, and I certainly did not want to die.

One of the significant happenings prior to my operation was the shunt that was put into my arm a week prior. It goes through the body and into the heart for readings to confirm if there's a problem. Actually seeing my heart on a big screen was interesting.

In 1976, I decided to have the heart valve transplant. I was given referrals to hospitals in Texas, California, and Alabama, and at the time, Alabama happened to be the teaching hospital for valve transplants. Since Alabama was close, I choose the University of Alabama Hospital, where Dr. Albert Pacifico performed the operation. The procedure involved cracking my rib cage and inserting a plastic valve, as opposed to using a pig valve. It left me in the hospital about five days and recovery was fine. In fact, the day I flew back home, I attended a party that evening.

Virtually, I haven't changed much of my lifestyle in order to stay healthy, although I do take Coumadin to avoid blood clots. I remain active to this day.

Listen to your doctor and follow his or her instructions. When I had my operation it was still a rare procedure, but today, heart valve surgeries are done virtually everywhere; it's really quite common. I've talked to many others who have had these transplants, and people who are going to have the transplant, and I try to reassure them that it's going to be fine; it will help.

I think I made the right choice. The doctors did a great job, and in the long run, it all worked out. Now things are good, and I have little or no awareness of my new heart valve except for a clicking noise from time to time. It's really quiet and others don't hear it as much as they used to.

If you're undecided about the operation and are given the choice between a lifestyle of restricted activity to a greater degree or one of an active, normal life, it seems like a no-brainer; go ahead and have the operation.

CHAPTER 11

Kidney Cancer and Disease

Gary Bear

CAN YOU IMAGINE YOURSELF GETTING a dialysis treatment three times a week in order for your kidneys to be able to function? Well, at first I couldn't imagine it either, but now, it's just a normal day-to-day part of my life.

It all started in 1992 with what could have been just a knee replacement for a sore ligament that was bothering me for years. Not that the surgery was simple by any means, because there wasn't a joint left in my knee anymore—hence the surgery—but I certainly did not expect to come out of that operation with news of a bigger illness. Nonetheless, after my knee replacement and during my rehabilitation, my right hand went numb. It continued to get worse, and I thought it must be because of the rehab. My doctor stepped in and suggested an MRI, which revealed a cyst in the spinal cord of my neck. That turned out to be what was giving me the numb sensation in my hand.

Soon after, I had a CAT scan, which found a growth on my right kidney. It turns out this growth had a cyst as well, except this cyst was cancerous. So once again another cyst was removed, but this

69

time the result was a hand that functions but will remain numb due to permanent damage.

It took another six years for my other kidney to lose function. Now, at seventy-two years old, I still have one functioning kidney, but it takes dialysis, a three and a half hour process, three times a week, to maintain it. When your kidneys don't function, everything gets screwed up. I take medications to control my phosphorus levels, and on top of that, I have been a diabetic for more than twenty years.

Dialysis takes a lot of time out of my life, but if I don't do it, I'll die. Not to say there are not days that are bad, but most days are fine after the almost four-hour treatment is done. The doctors have to keep close tabs on my blood levels.

In order to stay healthy, I work around the house and remain active at the Yankee Air Museum in Belleville, Michigan, helping around there to fix things up. I'm also on the list at the University of Michigan to receive a kidney transplant.

But the truth is, without the treatments my life would have more freedom: I could go up north like I want to and things would not be so restricted. Take my recent family reunion in Tennessee—for that trip alone I had to get dialysis set up there, but it turns out the system is well-connected across the country.

My lifestyle was different before I had kidney cancer; I could take off and go, but now I need to make the proper arrangements because nothing can be spur-of-the-moment. And other than my regular dialysis on Mondays, Wednesdays, and Fridays, that's really where the differences lie between my regular life and that of one with dialysis. I'm also more tired because those treatments can take a lot out of you. Some days I'm mildly tired, but for the most part, I feel good. What helps is that the people who handle the dialysis treatments are wonderful and treat you well.

So my message to all of you is don't give up hope. I've been fortunate that my personal doctor was great; he could talk to you and know that something wasn't right, and if he hadn't done that with me, who knows what could have happened? There were no symptoms that I had kidney cancer, so when the doctors tell you to do something, do what you need to do, do what they tell you to do, and most importantly, ask a lot of questions.

Oh, and if you are going to have kidney failure, make sure it happens when you're in your twenties.

MaryAnn Bear

It may sound strange to some, but I actually had a vision, more like a voice, come to my mind to tell me where my kidney transplant was coming from. It entered my thoughts that the kidney I desperately needed would come through. Two days later, I received a phone call that someone needed a new tennis racket, one I happened to have, and this took me through Dexter, Michigan, past the kidney-shaped pond from my vision. That was when I heard from the University of Michigan Hospital that a kidney was available. And that was not even the first kidney I ever received.

You see, ever since I was eighteen months old, I have experienced health issues. As a baby, I was scalded from my head to waist with hot water that left me with second- and third-degree burns, as an adult I got rheumatoid arthritis, and finally, my kidney eventually failed on me.

I started getting emotional at the time my daughter was graduating from high school, but looking back, that had been a sign. Coinciding with graduation, I was also having work done on the house, which involved the use of toxic chemicals, and for whatever reason, I started getting weird sensations. What got me in to see the doctor, however, was a tick bite. Once there I was told that my protein levels were high, which sent me to a neurologist about my kidneys.

A couple of years went by, but I was still carrying a lot of fluid. I was exercising, doing things naturally, but I began experiencing shortness of breath. That led me immediately to the hospital, where I was told I was a day away from death. Meanwhile, in the waiting room, I saw a little child who was actually dying, and that was when it hit me: I wanted to take my life back. So when the doctors took me in, I was not fearful; I was okay with things; I was at total peace. The next thing I knew, I was on life support.

Recovery took about two weeks in intensive care and totaled about a three-month recovery stay. Life still carried on, and for me, that meant moving out of our house and dealing with the Christmas season. It gets emotional even talking about it now.

Once settled, I started to receive dialysis, and at the time I thought, *Do I have to do this?*, but I knew I had to make it into a positive note, so I organized my time during the process to make it easier. After a little more than a year, my doctor told me I would do well with a kidney transplant, so I was put on the list. My rare blood type (AB positive) allowed the process to go quickly, and five months later, I received my first kidney transplant. This was 1987.

Now, nineteen years later, I had a terrible fall that broke my shoulder in five places. But the real kicker is that I may have jarred or shocked my kidney in the process. I was never told one way or another, but I noticed that was when things started to go wrong.

Once again I started collecting fluid; then I got a case of pneumonia that sent me to the hospital. All this meant another round of dialysis, except this time I went in thinking, *I will get a kidney; I will have a new life; I will go on.*

I may have waited more than two years for another kidney, which I received in 2008, but I believed I would get one, on God's terms, and it would be right. In the meantime, I worked at keeping others in the hospital unit happy and comfortable; other people like me.

After my second transplant surgery, I was home about five to six days later, and I started walking a mile a day. Today I still continue to walk and take medication, and overall, life is good. I try to look at life in a positive light with everything. This second kidney is no comparison to the first one; I feel great.

I have my quiet and peaceful time in my rose garden, and my log home is surrounded by luscious trees; I love nature. I also keep my hands busy by watercolor painting and knitting hats for infants at the hospital. My transplant has allowed that and put me on the road to help other people.

Yes, life was different when I was raising kids; it was more stressful, so this was a change in life for me to step back and realize what is important, what is not, what you feel comfortable with, and when you are not afraid to say no, you will be a lot stronger for it. Roadblocks make each of us stronger each time, and each time you move to the next level, so be thankful.

The doctors are required to tell you everything about your illness and that can be scary, but do not let that scare you; go for it; see it as an opportunity coming your way.

Now I can say my life is full and beautiful, and I want to share that with others; I will always be on that road. Remember, never fear, take each day as you go, and face your experiences, even if they are scary. Go forward and think you can do it. There is always a light ahead.

ॐ

Gary Gauger

I am a fortunate man, in the sense that my brother was a perfect match for my kidney donation. However, I'll start from the beginning, where it really all started, at the time when my daughter passed away from cancer.

Rachel was born with a genetic syndrome, resulting in a defective chromosome that left her unable to ward off cancer. In 2001, she went in for what she thought was a root canal but actually turned out to be a brain tumor. The oral surgeon noticed something wrapped around the nerve, and after an accidental MRI of the upper jaw (it was supposed to have been the lower), a brain tumor was revealed. Surgery was performed to remove the tumor, but during all this, there were also lumps found in her breasts. Rachel had both a double mastectomy and part of her jaw removed to rid the cancer. All in all, she had a year of chemotherapy and non-eventful happenings, until she had a seizure at age twenty-nine.

This condition is either genetic or a fluke, and we think it was a fluke because no one else in the family, on either side, has had this condition. The brain tumor came back, and in total, Rachel had seven different brain tumors. Once the cancer reached her brain stem, there was no hope after that. In 2006, she passed away. As if her family didn't endure enough at this point, after that, her husband was diagnosed with colon cancer. He went in for surgery to have his intestines removed, but the cancer had spread to his liver and lungs, and to this day, the cancer seems to come back each year.

I'm telling the prior happenings because the stress of all these incidents is what led to my conditions. As a diabetic, I was feeling rundown from work and stressed after the death of my daughter, and a trip to the hospital revealed my blood sugar levels had gone wild. My doctor was afraid to tell me after that blood test that my kidneys had failed. I did more than two years of dialysis, which took three and a half hours at a time for them to drain and filter my blood. I knew something wasn't right and that eventually I would need a new kidney.

My brother said he would donate his kidney, and I was approved as a recipient at the University of Michigan Hospital. However, there was a period of time when my brother changed his mind, but he eventually came back, said he did want to donate the kidney, and this time he felt it was for the right reason. I told my brother that I didn't want to climb this ladder with him only to have him change his mind, but when we finally started the process in January 2009, he never missed an appointment. He had to change his lifestyle because he was living on unhealthy foods, but this time around, he was committed.

The next six months had its ups and downs, but on June 10, they removed my brother's kidney. After a well-performed surgery, I woke up thinking, *Is this the same body I woke up with this morning?* because right away, I could feel the new kidney working. I thought about Rachel as I cried because I couldn't believe this was happening.

I was in the hospital for about four days and then went to the clinic for the next two months to make sure my body was accepting the new organ. Scar tissue ended up developing in my urethra, which caused an obstruction in my bladder, but after a stent was put in for six weeks, the blockage was relieved. I take Prograf, an anti-rejection medication, daily, and I will have to take it for the rest of my life. I also joined a gym and just continue to put my life back together because I'm still grieving for Rachel; that will never go away.

This wasn't my first major surgery either, because in 2004, I had a quadruple bypass, which was almost tougher than the kidney transplant. It took seven weeks of recovery for that operation, but I went back to work following thereafter.

Before I was diagnosed with kidney failure, I was so engrossed in Rachel's health there were some days I didn't even want to answer the phone because of what was going on. I felt like a pancake burnt on both sides; I went through unemployment, health battles, and then physically had to heal, but life is different now. Until you go through it, you never really know, but there is nothing I would have done differently. If my brother hadn't donated his kidney, I would still be getting dialysis and on the waiting list. Once you have kidney failure, there is no other choice besides dialysis or a new kidney. Eventually, this kidney will be rejected, but I could get another possible twenty years.

Now I'm doing well, living one day at a time, and figuring out what to do. I have gone back to the kidney center to visit other patients because I witnessed some difficult things in there. But here I am, almost sixty-five years old and looking for a quality of life. You want some level of normalcy, but if you don't have your health, you have nothing. Take care of yourself, listen to your doctor, and pay attention to your lifestyle, because that comes first. In my case, was it a job or life? I found that life comes first; a job is a job that you should enjoy. I was a corporate guy, on the fast track, but different things mean more to me now. If it wasn't for Lynn, my wife of twenty-six years, and my brother, I wouldn't be here right now. Economically, I am somewhere between living to work and working to live.

Often times, I think, *Why not my daughter instead of me; why did God not take me instead?* But I never get an answer. I get emotional when I think about this, and I remember Rachel telling me she didn't want to die; I will never forget that, but on a happier note, she tried to add humor by saying she should have been making babies, not tumors.

If I hadn't had a transplant, I couldn't have worked any more, I would be housebound, and mentally, I would be in a depression. I need stimulation both mentally and physically, and I would have deteriorated mentally more than physically. I don't want to think about it, but when people say they have their life back, they truly do.

CHAPTER 12

Leukemia

Ralph Bear

IN 1996, I WAS SENT to an oncologist, because I was told my white blood cell count had reached thirty-five thousand and was climbing. Normal is ten thousand. The oncologist showed me my medical report. On the bottom right-hand corner were the letters "CLL."

I asked him what that stood for. He said, "Chronic lymphocytic leukemia."

"What is chronic lymphocytic leukemia?" I asked.

He explained that it was a condition that had been caused by my high white blood cell count. Further, he elaborated, if my count reached one hundred twenty-five thousand, I would need chemotherapy. He checked my lymph glands to see if they were swollen. They weren't. He checked to see if my spleen was swollen. It wasn't. Physically I felt fine. But, he insisted, he knew I had CLL.

The first question out of my mouth was the last question I wanted to ask: How long do I have?

He told me a story about another patient who had CLL. This patient's white blood cell count went to one hundred thousand and stayed there for years. It never changed. I asked what his symptoms were. He said there were none. "He's fine." I repeated my first question: "How long do I have?" He looked away for a brief moment and then turned back toward me, but with vague eyes. He said I'd probably be dead by the time I was sixty-five and that there was only a 5 percent chance I would make it to age seventy.

I was fifty-six at the time and not ready to call it quits. Even seventy fell far short of my life's vision. "What can I do to strengthen the odds?" I asked.

His answer: "Nothing." But he said I should come back in a year.

Nothing? Boy did that piss me off! At the same time, I was scared silly and began one hundred twenty days of panic. I thought I was going to die. I started getting my affairs in order. I have a terribly close family, with a wife and children, so when I first found out, I wasn't secretive about it. Their support gave me strength.

But that wasn't enough. It was fortunate that I already was a regular at my local indoor tennis club. I paid them a visit the next day and told the pros there that we were going to beat this thing. I was going to attack it as an athlete. I had already been watching Lance Armstrong and knew of his success in beating his cancer. I hired an extra pro and began playing three or four days a week with him. I used to play baseball, so I knew the value of warming up the big muscles: legs, arms, biceps, triceps. So I practiced serving for forty-five minutes by myself. Then I would bring in the professional. We'd hit it back and forth for a half hour and then play a non-competitive game for a half hour. Basically, he would hit it in my range so I could get a workout. What I work for during tennis practice is a good sweat, because I found I felt better if I had a good sweat. I found that out by listening to my body.

While playing I drank a bottle of G2 Gatorade and a bottle of water. G2 is the lightest form of Gatorade and has a little potassium and a little nutrition. Drinking the water is like taking an internal shower. And I drank a pot of coffee in the morning before I started. Coffee is a strong antioxidant and one of the strongest diuretics in the business. Also, I stopped drinking alcohol because it disrupts your metabolism and dehydrates the brain.

A lot of recovery is about getting your rhythm back. I believe cancer survivors are people who got hold of this sucker early enough to cut out the worrying. Set a rhythm and run it out of town. A cancer cell is "frightened," so it's going to reproduce its way out of trouble. What do you do to tell your cells to calm down? We know that our big muscles, when used for activities like skiing, swimming, and running, boost our endorphin level, and we feel good. With my endorphins up, I was detoxifying myself. And I was having fun. If we're having fun, we do much better.

This is why I would like every CLL patient, and everyone who is living with an incurable condition, to know what I know. Don't panic. Be less scared. If I'm on red alert, my endorphins are ready for attack, but you can't be in attack mode all the time. You have to calm it down, de-stress, and laugh a lot. So during my workouts I drive people nuts because I engage in conversations with others. I'm there to have a good time. If a woman goes by and she's cute, I tell her. Does it hurt anyone? No, because when you're seventy you can do that and no one cares. And she feels good.

One of the gals checking my MRI and CAT scan is adorable. She says I have the brain of a forty-four-year-old. I say, really, what are you doing for lunch Thursday?

We also need to respect our brain and let it work at full strength, always, but especially during recovery. No image, no pretend; stay calm. A brain is probably growing at 8 percent a year. If we let the brain think its way out of a problem, the amygdala— the fear center—will find solutions. One way I do that is by writing for an hour every morning to calm my brain.

And in the process, you outlive the cancer.

By the way, I never did go back to see the oncologist who said I had a 5 percent chance of making it to seventy. I never saw him again. I don't mean disrespect for the guy, but I figured out a life-saving protocol without his help.

My routine stayed the same from the start, and I found another doctor who understood what I was doing and why. I never had symptoms, and once I started my warm-up routine, I even stopped the wheezing I used to do while I was playing. My white blood cell count continued to rise until it hit sixty-two thousand, but eventually it stabilized and decreased.

It's held steady at fifty-two thousand for the last seven years. And I turned 72 on April 24, 2011.

CHAPTER 13

Liver Cancer

Don Bear

BACK IN THE SEVENTIES, I was diagnosed with hepatitis C, but I lived with this for many years. Through those years, I was put on different medications, but it wasn't until recently that I had a scare, when it was discovered I had liver cancer.

When I was younger, I had a blood transfusion, and that's where the doctors believe my cancer came from. Prior to this, though, I was told, after a physical exam, that the enzymes in my liver did not look right. And just a few months ago now, a new doctor spotted something unusual with my blood work, which meant I was to be sent off for an ultrasound and an MRI (magnetic resonance imaging). It turns out she was right; something was wrong, because three lesions were found on my liver.

The procedure I had is not a cure by any means, but it's the best procedure they have to treat liver cancer. The process is to go into the blood vessels and hit the area of lesions in the liver with chemotherapy. It also cuts off the blood supply to the lesions so the cancer can't survive. It just so happens the doctors got all three lesions and were happy with the results. Yet after a follow-up MRI, something was found yet again, and another procedure had to take place. Even today, as I sit here explaining my story, I'm waiting to hear the results from my most recent MRI and learn what will happen next. But so far, things are good as I continue to wait and hear.

I've been fortunate because I don't have a lot of pain. I work out to stay healthy and feel good, but even through all this treatment I never vomited, felt nauseous, or had any symptoms as such that people might normally go through on chemotherapy, probably because it was a localized treatment. It's a quick procedure; they just have to keep you overnight at the hospital.

I think now, if I didn't do the treatment, I don't know, I'm certain the cancer would have spread. I can't say for sure, but when I talk to the doctors, they don't get all upbeat. If I need another treatment, yes, I'll go back in again, but I'm keeping my fingers and toes crossed.

This treatment may not be a cure-all, but if it can help people from feeling bad, I would tell them to go for it.

CHAPTER 14

Lung Cancer

John Changas's Wife

IF YOU KNEW JOHN, YOU would have seen what an amazing person he was: always active, a cook, a sewer, a fixer of cars; he could do anything. The one thing he couldn't do, however, was beat lung cancer.

For about two years, John was "doctoring." They didn't find anything wrong, but they didn't perform any tests. I think the doctors missed the boat on that one.

John then caught a cold that wouldn't go away, so he went to a doctor close to us, where they did blood work and an X-ray on his chest. Those tests revealed a tumor in his lungs. At the same time he was also sent to the hospital to be treated for pneumonia, and another X-ray found tumors in his liver, the source of the cancer. He was quickly sent to a clinic for biofeedback therapy, which cleared him of both tumors in the liver.

In another twist to the story, while doctors were performing the tests, they found asbestos in his liver, which they decided was probably the cause of his lung cancer. It made sense because he worked as an engineer doing industrial repairs on large equipment, but by that time the diagnosis was too late. It was those two years

83

of doctoring with no results that caused the disease to spread to his bone from the liver, into his lungs, and then finally into his brain.

All in all, this happened within eight months, and we lost him in January 1985.

John was sweet, loved me to death, and we did many things in those short nineteen years we were together. He was truly an outrageous, uninhibited person. If I had advice for people from his story, I would say take marijuana for medicinal purposes because the studies I have seen shows it to be safer than some medications.

꿈

Pat Bear

My sister didn't die for just any reason, which is why I share her story today. I couldn't say anything to her about quitting smoking, but now I wish I could have sent her a note to show her my concern; however, now it's too late.

My older sister and I could have had a closer relationship, but because of this, we didn't. She smoked three packs a day for almost forty-one years. Sure, there are warning labels that warn us not to, and many believe we all have (dormant) cancer in our bodies waiting to become active, so it makes sense that if you smoke, cancer will take over and settle in the weak spots.

Pat developed a cough. I remember standing outside my cousin's house with Pat as she puffed away, hacking. That cough turned into pneumonia, and the doctors wanted to go in for a biopsy of her lungs; not a good sign. The doctor was frank with her and told her he planned to test the biopsy but that it looked like cancer, and he warned her not to build up her hopes.

At the time, her two daughters seemed to be very optimistic about things, but later it was her daughters, primarily Michele, who became Pat's caregivers. In 2001, my fifty-three-year-old sister was diagnosed with lung cancer, which meant removing the right lung in an attempt to get rid of the cancer.

Michele researched lung cancer online because she wanted my sister to be near her family yet have the best treatment locally. But sometimes you just can't be successful in treatment. You also don't think there are others out there like you because you believe you're the only one going through this. The specialist at the University of Michigan Hospital removed her right lung and wanted to enlist Pat in a five-year study to show how people of lung cancer survived with having their lung removed. She was considered a success due to the removal of the cancer. The doctors thought she was going to survive, but they were wrong.

After the surgery, Pat was getting better and stronger, was building herself up, and was able to breath with only one lung. She was, however, in a wheelchair for about thirteen months after and things never really got better. She kept experiencing pain in her leg, and the doctors didn't know what was wrong. Five months later, a bone scan showed the cancer had not spread to her bones. But Pat knew something was wrong, insisting it was not right, and the doctor even suggested she go see a psychiatrist because she didn't have bone cancer.

Shortly after, through what I call divine intervention, Pat fell and broke her leg, which led her to receive another bone scan, and the cancerous spots were discovered. The cancer was literally eating away at her bones, and within five months, it had eaten through her femur bone. She went through radiation and chemotherapy, which seemed to be going well and made things better, yet she was still in pain. After that mishap, my sister watched her test results very carefully because she did have bone cancer, and because of doctor error, it had not been detected or treated earlier.

Pat then sought out the expertise of a bone cancer specialist, who informed her the next step would be to remove everything that was cancerous and reattach the femur bone. The specialist said he would even have her walking again after a few days (mind you, she hadn't walked in at least a year). Unfortunately, Pat had a blood clot, which meant she had to have surgery again, and she later dislocated her leg while recovering at home and had to have emergency surgery once again. Three surgeries within a one-month span took their toll, and after eight days in hospice, Pat passed away at age fifty-five.

My father had a cancerous lung tumor, went into a coma, and within a few days passed away. My mother-in-law also had lung cancer, went on oxygen, and very slowly, she passed away. My sister quit smoking in February 2001 and then had her right lung removed two months later and survived. And my niece quit smoking when she saw what happened to her mother. My point is, if someone asks you not to smoke, don't be insulted, because the person asking may be my sister or someone like her who just needs to breathe.

If I ask you not to smoke, it's because I love my family and believe that no one should smoke. Being a non-smoker, I respect those who are trying to quit. I too was in this position at one time, and after failing several times, I was able to quit. I am, however, having difficulty respecting smokers who refuse to respect me in that regard. A mistake we make about smokers is that whoever gets lung cancer deserves it because they smoke. Yet there are people who have never smoked a day in their life who get lung cancer. Do they deserve it? The fact is, no one "deserves" lung cancer.

On Pat's headstone we put *She was a courageous fighter*, because she was; she never wanted to give up. The whole experience leaves you with that feeling. Pat was an excellent patient and did everything the doctors told her to do, but she got cheated and didn't get to see her daughters get married or see her grandchildren. I think about how my sister was at least blessed, though, with her two daughters Julie and Michele, and her life, even though she missed a lot.

What enabled me to be with her through the illness was meeting all the wonderful people along the way that I didn't even know existed. While you're enduring your burden, let the good people you meet keep you strong; that's something I learned. I want people to think about this; think about what they're doing.

The good memories are what keep you going, so make sure to share them, because if someone's feeling bad, it may be a laugh or a simple smile that makes their day and makes them feel that much better.

CHAPTER 15

Lupus

Thelma Bear

BY THE TIME ONE REACHES eighty-seven years old, there comes the realization that life consists of changes. Hence the need for one adjustment after another. Fortunately, as human beings, the ability to adapt is our long suit. Thus we find new ways to go, or, as is often said, *new paths to trod*. And often the discovery keeps us going.

Arthritis is a creepy thing, and I mean that literally. It creeps up on one over the years. I first noticed mine when I was in my fifties. I walked and followed a careful, healthful diet. Nevertheless, by the time I was sixty-four I had two hip replacements. Upon recovery, I walked and followed a healthful diet. Heredity, however, was putting up a good fight, and as I got along in my eighties, I was diagnosed with spinal stenosis. That was controlled through water therapy, but that is another story.

This winter, I was diagnosed with lupus. The main effect for me is arthritis. Even though I sometimes feel that I am turning to stone, persistently doing water and easy land exercises helps. I use a cane, but I can drive, take care of myself, shop, go to movies, the theatre, museums, visit with family and friends, and I live alone. In a way, limited movement gives me more time for reading, writing, and keeping up with family and friends through the computer, the telephone, and cell phone. I am slower to get things done, but hey, what's the hurry?

Could I do it without the loving support of my family? I don't know. Right now I feel that I can get through most days—not every day, but most days—feeling I have fulfilled a few necessary, worthwhile, and lofty accomplishments. And fun.

CHAPTER 16

Lymphoma

Catherine Bear's Husband

EVEN TELLING HER STORY NOW still brings tears to my eyes, because Catherine was such a beautiful person. It has been more than ten years since she passed away from non-Hodgkin's lymphoma, but the memory remains the same. And it did not start with that form of cancer either.

The first signs of health problems came about in 1980, during a time that she had two young children. Catherine complained of headaches and changes in her forehead, but the doctors seemed to brush it off as changes she was going through. I remember Catherine getting upset, because the doctors just were not getting it.

Eventually, Catherine went in for a biopsy, where the doctors made a small incision right above her eyebrow; however, once inside, they closed up the incision fairly quickly and told her to get to the hospital immediately because what they saw was the bone deteriorating. It turns out that deterioration was a very rare form of cancer in the upper sinuses and what it does is eat away the bone, leaving damage. Catherine was lucky nonetheless, because even though it was quite a procedure she went through, the doctors were able to take all the bone out, rid her of cancer, and make an eventual permanent prosthesis of the sinus bone area. Those doctors did such a good job, you would have never known she had a prosthesis because she never lost any of her beauty.

After that, Catherine was in remission for thirteen years. She started her own business counseling the elderly, she volunteered for the American Cancer Society, and she raised her children with love and compassion; she was something, all right. It wasn't until those thirteen fateful years later that cancer hit her again, and this time with a vengeance, in the form of non-Hodgkin's lymphoma.

From there she endured doses of chemotherapy and radiation treatments; you could not believe what she went through. Catherine was in and out of the hospital, but even through it all, her tough persona never complained or let the pain show to her five children, because to them, their mother was everything. But her luck faded fast, and in 1998, at age sixty-one, she passed away.

I would tell others do not give up, to keep up the fight, because Catherine was in remission for thirteen years; that is a very long time and that makes it hard, but it also makes it better too.

Today, Catherine would be seventy-three years old. At the time of her illness, I remember her telling me that she just wanted to live long enough to see her youngest son get his driver's license, and she did.

❧

Michelle Seluk

I never really thought of this at the time I was diagnosed with Hodgkin's lymphoma, but I've always been a more optimistic than pessimistic person, not so much that I was making a conscience effort to be, but that is just the way I am. That positive mood, I do believe, can help improve an outcome of a diagnosis.

In March 2007, I went to my doctor for what I thought was strep throat because I could feel bumps. My doctor did not see any bumps in my throat, but he did see swollen lymph nodes. I remember feeling tired, but I thought it was from feeling kind of down from my previous unemployment and the transition into a new job. I wasn't sure if it was my mood or my health. That day I was prescribed an antibiotic to take the swelling down in my lymph nodes and was told to come back in a couple of weeks.

A month later, the bumps were still there, and although it was believed it was probably nothing, I was still sent to see the ears, nose, and throat doctor. The doctor decided to do a needle biopsy on the swollen lymph node, and the test result came back negative. A couple of months went by and I went in again, this time to test a circular lymph node that I could feel. I probably wouldn't have noticed it if the doctor hadn't pointed it out, and it didn't hurt. But when I drank alcohol, I could feel the swollen lymph nodes more (something that turned out to be a symptom of Hodgkin's lymphoma).

The second biopsy also came back negative, but the doctor honestly felt that it didn't look right, so he proceeded to do a full biopsy to take the entire lymph node out. It was a painful procedure that left me very swollen and stuck indoors because I didn't want to go anywhere. However, the following Monday, I was back at work and received a call from my doctor stating he wanted me in that afternoon, right away. I had a bad feeling; I knew this wasn't good. The biopsy came back with Hodgkin's lymphoma cells, and I was diagnosed with the cancer in November 2007.

My thoughts were confused because I was told I have a "little bit of cancer" in my body—so did I or didn't I? My doctor was making it sound like it wasn't a big deal. I wasn't sure what to think; I didn't think it was cancer, but I was so confused. Something that made me feel some reassurance, though, was how my doctor said that if I were to have cancer, this was the one to have, because it is the only cancer that can be considered cured once it's in remission.

However, it didn't quite comfort me, and as I sat in the doctor's office shocked, scared, and crying, I wished I had someone there with me. I felt weird, and even the nurses felt bad, as they'd had to give me the news while I was all by myself. I received a prescription for sleeping aids, which at the time I thought was strange because I didn't know how hard this was going to be to deal with. My husband was at work, so I didn't want to call him, so I called my mom and she too was shocked by the results.

By the time my husband got home, he seemed more surprised than I was because he wasn't certain that cancer was a possibility. Not much later, I met with an oncologist for staging a CAT scan, a PET scan, and a bone marrow test. Thankfully, nothing had spread to the bone, and my cancer was in stage one A, which is even better than stage one. My doctor also said he was confident that I would be taken care of and will move on with my life. This will just be something from the past.

After a second opinion, I proceeded with both chemotherapy and radiation treatments. I started treatments after the Christmas holiday, took time off from work with the special-needs children, and received chemotherapy for about eight weeks. Everyone knew who I was in there because I was one of the two younger women getting treatments at the time. Chemotherapy was strange and took a while to get use to, but typically I would feel pretty good after and then a little crummy for a couple days.

After a couple rounds of chemotherapy, my hair started to fall out, and the hair all over my body started to thin. The hair on my head never completely fell out, but it thinned out pretty bad and left a bald spot where the radiation directly hit. When it became too much, I even had a shaving party with my husband, where we both shaved our heads bald. It was weird to have no hair, but also a convenience because when you wear wigs, you can take your hair off and on, and style it up accordingly. My hair did, however, grow back within a couple months after radiation.

My blood count overall was pretty good, and following chemotherapy, I had radiation five days a week for about three weeks. A mold of my body was made for the treatment; that way I was in the exact same position. The treatment didn't hurt so much, but after two weeks, the throat pain got worse, almost like you had a sunburn in your throat. I remember eating a piece of pineapple after, which was a bad idea; the acidity of the fruit burned my throat.

During my radiation, I received another PET scan, and the results showed that the cancer was gone and I could finish my treatment. Prior to, my doctor mentioned freezing my eggs because chemotherapy could make people infertile. I did want to have children some day, so I considered the process, but after speaking with my gynecologist, it was recommended that I didn't need to because of my age and type of cancer. I was told I should be just fine to have children once I was cancer-free for a year. Following the one-year mark, and just one month later, I was pregnant with my first child.

Every three months, I get a thorough check of my body and lymph nodes, and my last PET scan was clear. Sometimes, I still freak myself out when I feel my lymph nodes or I feel tired, and I think, *Oh, no, it's back.* Every little thing, you tend to think maybe that's it. Now, though, I am pregnant with my second child, and every six months I will continue to go in for a cancer check-up.

I am also now considered to be in remission and have read that I can be considered cured, but the doctor hasn't told me that yet. You always want to think that you can be cured, but you can always get something else. But I do feel very lucky. Another Hodgkin's lymphoma patient, a woman older than I, once told me that I was lucky to have the disease now, and at all, because it will help me grow and that I will change from this experience. At the time I thought it was strange, but now it makes sense, and I can appreciate the experience I have been through.

This also made me think about what I put into my and my child's bodies, and where cancer even comes from. I try to avoid ingredients like high fructose corn syrup and artificial sweeteners, and I eat fewer processed foods and use better skincare products too. Since I wonder where I got cancer from, I eliminate as many probable causes as I can think of. During treatments, I also incorporated ways to detoxify my body with wheatgrass shots and Kombucha (fermented tea) drinks. Also, I make sure to stay active.

I would tell others who have Hodgkin's lymphoma to keep a positive attitude, because stress and depression can take a toll on the body. Also, make plans of what you will do later, because this is just a bump in the road; it is not the end-all be-all.

CHAPTER 17

Melanoma

Brad White's Daughter

 IF MY FAMILY AND I learned anything about my dad's diagnosis of melanoma, it was, and is, to get internal check-ups, but that is something doctors did not tell us; rather, it was something we found out along the way.

Seven years ago, my dad had a mole removed from the top of his head, which was tested and came back positive for melanoma. After the mole was removed, tests were also performed on his lymph nodes, which checked out good; therefore, other than routine skin checkups every three months, there was no need to be alarmed because he thought he was fine.

What happened next, however, was something we did not see coming. The cancer may not have spread on the outside, but it did spread on the inside, which is why internal check-ups—a CAT scan or something—is of utmost importance.

The symptoms came on slow. We noticed my dad was sleeping more and more, something out of the norm for this hardworking man, and he was complaining of stomach pain. He was also getting headaches, which was unusual because he never really used to get them. My dad was always on the go, so we knew it was strange to see him sleeping so much.

At first my dad was diagnosed with depression, but we knew that was not the case. The doctors also thought it might have been multiple sclerosis (MS), but they could not pinpoint anything until a CAT scan showed spots on his liver. A biopsy was also done and confirmed the melanoma had indeed spread from one spot to another.

On June 2, 2010, he was officially diagnosed with metastasized melanoma, and it was too late. The scary part was that seven years prior, his lymph nodes came back clean; he was told he was fine, so we never really knew this could recur, people can never really know, unless you get all the proper tests done. That is what's scary.

His first treatment was radiation because the cancer had spread to his brain (even though his liver was the worst hit out of all his organs); however, when he was done with radiation, the cancer was too far along (they could not do the chemotherapy during this form of radiation). Shortly after, the doctors told us there was nothing more they could do for my dad.

He was able to come home a week following that, but once his potassium levels became unstable, he was back in the hospital. Nine days later, my dad passed away.

There is not a day that goes by that I do not think about him, but if I could tell you all something, it would be that even though the tests come back negative, you should still get an entire body scan even if your insurance does not pay for it because this situation can happen to anyone with this type of cancer. Also, this cancer does not show up in blood work; he had blood work done over and over and nothing showed up. My dad needed to get a CAT scan every couple of years; I believe this would have helped; they could have caught it earlier.

Prior to his first diagnosis with melanoma, my dad was outdoors a lot, playing sports, but after he had his mole removed he made it a point to always wear sunscreen. He did what he was supposed to do and what he was told to do by the doctors.

This just so happens to be a really sneaky form of cancer; with other cancers, you may get noticeable symptoms, but for my dad, this was not the case. People need to know these things, because my dad, he was not so lucky, but maybe if just one other person in a similar situation can read this, he or she will know and it could change the outcome.

Jack Apple

I was eight years old when I was diagnosed with melanoma cancer, so really, a lot is hard for me to remember about how I felt at the time. However, now at fifteen, and as a cancer survivor, I can say that I don't worry about it too much because I think if you do, you let the cancer beat you.

It all started with a childhood wart on my ear. It was frozen off but came back twice as big; and then, after a biopsy was performed, we found out it was melanoma. The doctors checked to see if the cancer had spread to my lymph nodes or into my neck because it was so deep. They checked about three or four times, and it came back positive, so they decided to do a total neck biopsy, which included removing all of my lymph nodes.

Following that, I was also told I should do chemotherapy to make sure it did not and would not spread, so, for about another month I had chemotherapy, and then shots three times a month for a year. Basically, after those treatments were complete, it was a matter of routine check-ups to make sure there were no more weird skin blotches. Now, since all of that, I can say I have been cancer free for about five years.

Without treatment, I would not be here today; that's how life would be now. If I could tell other kids going through what I did just one message it would be to stay positive and confident about your treatment. That's what I did. Now I can continue to be a kid, and a pretty cool kid, if I say so myself.

CHAPTER 18

Mental Illness

Alaina Bear's Sister

IF I COULD MAKE ONE wish and only one wish for my little sister, it would be that she didn't have schizophrenia.

Easy to say, yes. But easy to see, hardly.

I can't give the exact date of when she was hit with this debilitating mental illness, but I can speak of the signs that, in retrospect, we (her family) can now tag to schizophrenia, but back then we had no clue what lay ahead.

My sister was officially diagnosed with schizoaffective disorder when she was twenty-one years old. It's scary to think that when most people are celebrating that yearly milestone in a different way, she was coming down with a mental illness.

At first the symptoms were mild: scattered thinking, irregular eating habits, and loss of focus and direction. Those all seemed like things that could be chalked up to lack of sleep or maybe being run down, or, worst-case scenario, an eating disorder. But not schizophrenia; anything but that.

Her situation became progressively worse. She was talking to herself about circumstances that didn't make sense; she was getting lost and was rapidly reducing in size because she was forgetting to eat. My parents didn't know what to think, but my older sister and I knew—no, we could feel—that something was wrong.

It wasn't long until my sister had her first psychotic breakdown, which left her in the hospital. I can remember being so numbingly scared, and then seeing her in there as if I was seeing a ghost. This wasn't my sister; not the fun-loving, caring yet goofy girl I grew up with. This was someone else.

But that is the past; today is different, and this is her future.

She is still a fun-loving, caring, and goofy girl, but she is a girl with a mental illness. She is that girl with a stigma attached to her that may never go away. She is a girl who, without proper medication, can't get through a "normal" day. She is a girl who is forever changed.

Each of my family members handle the illness in their own ways, I suppose. My mom, her primary caregiver, is forever testing her patience yet is there for my sister's every need. My dad also helps to support my sister yet still struggles to accept her new reality. As for my older sister, she is the voice of reason. And me, well, after many years, numerous doctors, countless hours of reading and research, and finally witnessing my sister through her struggles, it has taken me a long time to accept her mental illness. I've come a long way from telling no one about her illness to now helping break the stigma.

Her symptoms, by definition, are classified as "negative" because of the lack of characteristics that should be there. They include emotional flatness, lack of expression, inability to start and follow through with activities, speech that is brief, and a lack of pleasure or interest in life. Nonetheless, through medication and the love of her family, she leads a good, simple life filled with activities she enjoys that bring her interest in life.

In a world where even scientists and doctors don't fully understand the illnesses of the brain, I can't imagine what goes through her head daily. Frankly, I don't think she fully understands her illness, although she does recognize "she's different than she was," by her definition.

I cannot explain it, but when you are faced with this kind of illness, your life does a 180, and either people are strong enough to face the hurdles or they are not.

Unfortunately, there are stigmas. There are people who just do not understand or do not want to understand. This is the world we live in; and yet, it's also the world my sister lives in.

The truth is, a mental illness can isolate young people, any people, because of a lack of understanding. If you do not understand someone who has an illness and what it means, you are only isolating them. Their brains work different; their thinking is different and not always clear, and for some, their memories are not the same as they used to be.

So what does my sister need now? She needs exactly what she gets: love, support, and friendship from her family, and enjoyment of life through arts, crafts, music, and us.

I know this article can never fully explain or show what it's like to live with a loved one who has a mental illness; nevertheless, one thing I can say is that you truly never know until you're in that situation.

There is not a day that goes by, or will ever go by, that doesn't pain me to see my sister this way. It was never planned, it was never brought upon, and there was nothing anyone could do.

There are many things that have changed, but there is one constant: she will always be my sister, who I love; that is a fact that no mental illness can ever take away.

CHAPTER 19

Multiple Sclerosis

Chris Bear

IT'S HARD TO DESCRIBE MY illness in just one sentence. I say this because it does things that knock you off your block—things you can't control and things you can't see.

About twelve years ago I was diagnosed with bipolar disorder, after I went through postpartum depression with my second child. I was in denial at first but went through a series of events: symptoms of highs and lows—highs that got erratic, eventually resulting in suicidal attempts from acting wild and heavy drinking of alcohol. During my state of denial my family and friends told me this was happening, but it turns out you sometimes find things out the hard way, and then you eventually surrender to it (bipolar disorder) because it really is a lifelong thing.

Within the last five years, I still see the effects as a woman forty-seven years old, but I seek treatment and am being compliant with my medication. However, I was no longer able to do what I had been doing before (I went from an executive vice president role to being on disability), although I am fortunate to have a diagnosed disability so I can figure out what to do next.

I was prescribed Lithium and Prozac, along with other medications, but my condition remained on and off. Although I'm taking my medication now, my condition still bounces around. My illness seems worst between November and February, with peak (bad) times in January and February. For me, the best time is being in cognitive therapy on a regular basis, where I can discuss mood charts, notice changes to become more in tune with my behavior, journal my thoughts, and see how things affect me.

My suicidal episode that sent me to the hospital was an eye-opening yet humbling experience because it allowed me to sit through sessions and see others who were going through what I was at the time. Complemented with the medication, I got help keeping my head up and not let myself get into a real high or a really *low* low. Bipolar is a disease you have to deal with every day; it's not going to go away; it will always be there.

Without the treatment, I probably would have committed suicide. The interesting fact about that is that I have two other siblings who did in fact commit suicide because maniac depression runs in the family.

For me, I survived because of my supportive family, the research I have done, and my spirituality. I have a disease that I have no control over, but I think there has to be a greater power than me helping out because I can't go through this alone. I have God in my life and I don't try to do it alone because I recognize my illness. However, this acceptance was not done overnight; it takes a while to accept the disease because your life gets compartmentalized. It's a tall order, but when you get older you realize that this is your life. God has handed me a life-changing event, and I'm growing today because of my illness.

It turns out God wasn't done there either, because about four years ago, I was diagnosed with multiple sclerosis (MS).

I was having issues of numbness and physically wasn't feeling right, so I had an MRI performed on my legs. Then, as I was driving in, I almost hit a motorcycle because all a sudden, my foot went numb. From there, everything happened very quickly, and strange enough, that feeling of *not right* did not go away, so I went to the emergency room for a brain scan and was told I had MS.

At this point, I thought, *What else can God give me?* But I went on with the steroids, more medication, a walking cane, and once again submerged myself into research about the disease. As with bipolar, there is no cure for MS, but I continue to take my injectable medication to help deal with the symptoms, and so far, by the grace of God, I'm okay.

The doctors are uncertain whether I can ever get off my medication for MS, and they wonder what would happen if I did, but to me it is not worth finding out. Just like any unpredictable disease, you get through it one day at a time. Physical activity helps get the inhibitors in the right place because exercise is the best thing for MS.

Although my first year of diagnosis was about waiting for an attack and to end up paralyzed and in a wheelchair, there is hope. You have to have hope. For me, if I didn't have God in my life, I would have given up, because managing a mental illness, let alone a second illness, is a full-time job.

I am still working on merging the two illnesses, but I don't have to do it alone. I'm being compliant with medication and doing things I need to do.

Before, life was different, more structured, but these experiences have made me grow up, and I look at my life more seriously now. For me, it's the importance of being there for my husband and children, finding a higher power, enjoying my dirt (gardening) therapy, and trying to focus and strengthen my inner self. Some days are hard and some are not, but it's still my life and I have to cope and deal with it. I believe there is a purpose in things that happen, this so happens to be mine.

❧

Kate Mulligan Bear

Multiple sclerosis (MS) is a mysterious disease. I say this because the symptoms are diverse with this disorder, which attacks the nerves of the eyes, brain, and spinal cord and then causes the scoliosis in that area. In other words, you short-circuit. MS affects people by alternating periods of good health and flair-ups, because really, no one knows why. I was diagnosed with this disease in 1988.

I felt the symptoms coming on one day as I was walking up a flight of stairs, when all of a sudden, my leg contracted going up and then did it again. I did not know what that could be so I went to get it checked out by a neurologist. The symptoms went away, but at the same time, I was dealing with my father-in-law's passing away suddenly after. Not long after I woke up one day, blind in my left eye. As a practicing nurse, I figured I had a tumor on my optic nerve, so I went to see an ophthalmologist, where I was tentatively diagnosed with optic neuritis. About a week or so later, my vision ended up coming back, but when I went to visit the doctor again, I was told I had MS.

At the time, I had a friend who was also diagnosed with MS, so it made sense to me. On the bright side, the doctor told me he did not think I would end up in a wheelchair (like so many others with the disease do).

After a while, the symptoms (such as numbness and tingling) went away altogether. But that is the thing about MS—it can come and go at any time and last any amount of time. It is scary, and while they have ideas of what the cause is, it is still not clear.

The next step was going to see a neuro-ophthalmologist for a CAT scan of my head. My other option could have been optic neuritis treatment, but I never did that because the doctors recommended medication for the treatment instead.

The lucky part is, since my diagnosis in 1988, I have pretty much been symptom free. Since stress can trigger the disease, I thought maybe my career as a nurse was affecting my MS, so I got out of the field. Now at fifty-nine, I am an Irish dancer, I play the harp, and I told myself I am not going to be in a wheelchair. This disease scared me and my husband to death, but point blank, I was not going to put up with it.

I love to remain active by playing golf, exercising, and walking. I consider myself lucky: lucky that I do not have to have treatments and lucky I do not have to be in a wheelchair. In order to get there, I knew I had to lose a lot of weight, so I did. I also worked on my brain by being positive and thinking, *I can make this go away.*

By taking the bull by the horns, I was able to not let MS run me; it is what helps. I deal with things as they happen and am lucky because it is a strange disease. With MS, you have a heck of a time with the vague symptoms, so you need to watch yourself and keep track. I do not necessarily think my life would be different, because there are people out there who have it a lot harder. One example is a friend of mine who was diagnosed with the disease, and she almost drove herself crazy. She would not listen to me as I told her she needed to take things on a daily basis, and it turns out she did not have MS after all.

Before, my lifestyle was not about paying attention to my nutrition and being stressed out. Sure, being a nurse for almost twenty years was a positive, but I moved on from there and retired as a nurse.

I say try to be strong. If you can help one other person, you'd better get out there and help because we can all have our fifteen-minute pity party, but then you move on. Take your body seriously, listen to it, and as good as the doctors may be, they do not know it all, so write things down, and go see somebody to share your symptoms. Time can be wasted and some things you can prevent, so be knowledgeable, go to support groups if you have to, talk to a friend, or even make up a song, such as I and a friend of mine did (we called ourselves the MS girls), because humor is sometimes the best medicine.

CHAPTER 20

Organ Donation

Duane Gauger

IT ALL STARTED IN JUNE 2008. My brother, Gary, and I were estranged for about twenty years because of a rough childhood, and unfortunately, we went our separate ways. We only kept in touch once in a while.

Our first contact after so many years happened when his daughter died of cancer. I attended the funeral and was able to reconnect with him there, but then that following June, I called Gary one day. That was when he told me his health was failing. He experienced a heart attack, and the long-term outcome was that due to his kidney failure, he would only have a few months to live; he was dying. I asked if there was anything I could do for him, perhaps donate a kidney, and that's when Gary just broke down crying. He didn't understand why, after so many years of not speaking, I would want to do that, but I volunteered.

In 2008, however, my life was different. I was doing bad things, and it was becoming a real problem. I still thought, *No big deal, I can do this, I can donate a kidney.* But this experience became a real eye-opener.

Two weeks later, I went in for testing to donate and basically received a line that I was an unworthy candidate due to the fact that I was a borderline diabetic and not the personality they were looking for; that was the eye-opener. I let Gary down and I let myself down. This is when it really hit me that I needed to improve my life, and the way I did was through God.

I always use to roll my eyes and was a nonbeliever, but I started going to church with my wife, and the humor and messages I found was exactly what I was looking for. I became baptized, which was life-changing, and went back to Gary in 2009 to tell him we needed to start the donor process again.

I started testing at Henry Ford Hospital in Detroit, and after three extensive months, I came back a magnificent specimen. This time around, I had my faith and family. I had one final test to go before clearance, which was a glucose sugar test. Mind you, I had been a courier for more than thirty-eight years, so I pretty much lived on a sugar-laden diet; therefore, my blood sugar was not what they wanted, and I failed the test.

I had two weeks to get my blood sugar below 100, so I exercised and, ate healthy but still couldn't get below 140. On the last day before I had to take the test, I checked my blood sugar level and it was 126, so I put on my sweats and went for a run. I tested my blood again when I got back, and this time it had shot up to 156, so I went out again for another run. Yet my blood was still 151. I just broke down after that because all I could think was that this wasn't going to happen, I wasn't going to be a donor. But I went out for a run one last time, and it was a miracle—my test came back at 96. This was it, I thought, my time to go in for the hospital test was now, so I registered 94 and another test after the sugar was processed, which also came back 94. Want to talk about miracles? That was it; I was accepted.

Two months later, the transplant was performed; Gary received my left kidney and it was a huge success. At that point, he had been on dialysis for the previous three years, and it wasn't working anymore so he needed this transplant. Now he has twenty-five more years, and I'm living the good life.

Both Gary and I have the rare O-positive blood type, so for me, this was a no-brainer. Within the first hour of his receiving the kidney, he was able to urinate properly and lose all the excess liquid in his system. I was also back at things within a week after the surgery.

After twenty years of not talking to my brother, there's not a day that goes by that we don't talk. If I didn't do this, Gary would be gone, and I would be devastated because I was his only hope. He didn't have any more time, so being a sibling, I jumped on it right away.

In my opinion, you are not going to donate an organ unless you have God's help. I'm one of those people who have to be shown. You don't have to be a religious fanatic, but if you ask for help, eat right, and live a good, clean life, you will get it. I never smoked, drank seldom, and lived a pretty clean life, and being an athlete helped in my favor. But I wasn't living the best life I could, and even my friends and family have seen the difference in me. Without my wife staying by my side, I would be different.

It took almost going through a divorce, dealing with upset children, and being claimed an *unworthy* donor to get there, but I wouldn't have done things any differently. After I was turned down as a donor, I knew what I had to do, and every day I got stronger.

Luckily, I was one of those guys who had never been sick a day in his life. Now I'm a spokesperson for the National Kidney Foundation, and I travel to various high schools to share my story. I love being called to speak and give testimony. I also stay healthy as a youth sports official, play ball with my friends, and watch my blood sugar levels and sugar intake.

Things are good now. I got involved, I help other people, and I manage to pay the bills every week, so to me, God does provide when you turn your life over to him; that's what I believe. Be an organ donor and get on the bandwagon to donate, because the life you're saving could be a family member's.

CHAPTER 21

Prostate Cancer

Bruce Bear

WHEN THE NURSE CALLED ME while I was at work and told me I had cancer, I nearly fainted. She said I needed to come in and decide what kind of method I wanted to use to *attack* the cancer, but all I could think at the time was that I needed to sit and think for a minute. I mean, this was serious stuff.

Since time is of the essence, I moved within a week to find the best place for treatment. At the time, my daughter was ill too, so it was important for me to still be able to work. My daughter had to have medical treatment and hospitalization, so I knew surgery would lay me up, and the recovery period would be longer. After talking it over with the surgeon, I decided to have implant radiation therapy, a low-dose form of radiation where seeds are implanted and are directed to burn the cancer.

The doctors first discovered I had prostate cancer in 2005 after a routine check-up. After a certain age, a prostate specific antigen (PSA) test is common and necessary for men, but as luck would have it, when I went in for my first test ever, it was found my protein was elevated in my prostate. I was then directed to see a urologist for further inspection, more tests (an MRI, CAT scan, and more), and a biopsy, which came back positive for cancer. Thankfully, my cancer was a low-rated one.

Radiation treatments took about thirty to forty days in a row and were not too painful or tiring. Other than the obvious cancer, I was considered to be in good health, so the radiation did not affect me too bad.

When the radiation was complete, the treatment was monitored through further PSA tests, which showed that the cancer did not spread. Doctors also put me on the medication Flomax to relax the nerves around the prostate so I could urinate properly. There was, however, a two-to three-week scare after the initial treatment was done because I had a collapsed prostate intestine that closed and locked. I could not urinate, so I had to have a catheter bag for a week as a method to reopen the intestine and stretch it back to its normal size, but that was a scary thing.

Now, in order to stay healthy, I continue to get a PSA test once a year, I eat a lot of fruits and vegetables (I still enjoy meat too, but not as much), and I have coffee (a great diuretic) in the morning. I also try to eat more fish and poultry and tend to lean toward a more vegetarian diet, if anything. I also needed to lose weight because of my blood pressure (which also increased when my daughter got sick and I got cancer).

Today, at age sixty-one, I am considered in remission, but you never really become cancer free. Life would have been a gamble without the treatment; it is an option, and another option is to not do anything, but I did not choose that option.

There was never a history of cancer in my family until I and my younger brother got sick. But I have to tell you that if you are in my position, do treatment as quickly as you can, whatever your option is. In my case, I did what I could to keep working and it did not change my lifestyle radically during or after. With surgery, some guys complain, but this was the best choice for me.

Before, my lifestyle was different because I had the laissez fare attitude that you do not think of those things; you take things for granted. This was my first look at mortality and it was a big eye-opener; you are not immortal and you can die. It is like one day you are well and then the next someone tells you that you are ill, and it makes you appreciate when you do feel good. If anything, it makes you appreciate being well.

ॐ

Jerry LeClerc

Looking back, I cannot imagine what would have happened if I had listened to the advice and waited a couple of years before treating my prostate cancer. And that was almost ten years ago.

Now, at age fifty-one, this Detroit native is in remission and living well. I can say this now. However, the details of a November 2010 physical would paint a different picture. They would color a trip to the physician who found something irregular, followed by a visit to the prostate doctor, which later led to the diagnosis of stage-three prostate cancer.

At first, the doctor told me I could go ahead and wait about four or five years before I acted on the cancer; but of course I did not want to do that. I wanted the cancer out of my body right away. I was given a choice between radiation or surgery. For me there was no choice; I chose surgery, and December 3, 2010, the cancer was removed.

The tricky part about prostate cancer is the little hair-like nerves around it that control urination and other bodily functions. Each one of those hairs controls something. This is important to note because unfortunately, many people have problems after this type of operation. I was fortunate because my operation went well; it came out fantastic, and I have not had any side-effects or symptoms of recurrence; basically, everything still functions properly.

At this point, you may be wondering, why am I telling you all this? Why such detailed information? That is simply because I want to get the word out about how things can go well, and if the prostate cancer operation is performed without damaging any of those nerves, there are usually no side-effects or problems.

The bottom line is, I did not want any cancer in my body. Maybe it is the fact that my mother and father both died of cancer, but there is not another way to say it: I did not want the disease in my body any longer.

I read a statistic somewhere stating "seventy percent of people who go through radiation for cancer have their cancer come back." That statistic alone is shocking enough for me to pursue the operation. I am not going to lie; the first four days after the surgery were terrible: a drainage tube in my body, a urine bag for about a month, and quite a bit of pain, but honestly, that was the worst of it all. After about two weeks, I was back on regular food and the pain was gone. It then took about six months before I could really become active again.

Today, there is still the fear of losing bodily functions from time to time; however, from then until now, I pretty much lead a normal lifestyle (although my bladder cannot hold as much liquid as it could prior to the operation). I eat differently than I did before, which means I have stopped drinking faucet (tap) water (I drink purified bottled water), and I live in the countryside of Ann Arbor, Michigan, where I exercise a lot more than I ever did. Most importantly, I pay attention to death now because it is constantly on my mind.

My message to you is, do not hesitate to get the cancer cut out of you as I did; go against the radiation because you can still be sexually active and maintain your bodily functions, which can be affected by radiation treatments. Also, always get a second opinion; that is my one regret because I did not, and if I could do it over, I would. A dear friend of mine did not receive a second opinion about prostate surgery and opted for radiation instead, and to everyone's horror, the cancer spread throughout his body. He passed away six months later. This is why I tell you, please, if nothing else, at least get a second opinion, and do not be afraid of the operation.

These details are not always pleasant, maybe even a little too graphic at times, which I kind of feel funny discussing, but it is my reality and has made me look at life differently. I use to be a *saver* and now I am a *spender*. Going through something like this really changes your outlook on life, at least for me it did; it really makes you think. Even though I know that one day we all are going to die, now, because of this, it is constantly on my mind. Without my treatment, I would have gone by life day-by-day not having a care in the world; in fact, I did not even think about death. Now I have more life insurance, for example, because an experience like this awakens things to scare you close to death.

This is not to say that I am not enjoying life more because I am. While I certainly think life was different before my diagnosis, I am now healthier, and I did not (and do not) want to miss one minute of that or my life.

CHAPTER 22

Skin Conditions

Emerson and Fionn Bears' Parents

OUR SONS ARE THREE AND one years old, and both were born with albinism. Wow, what happened? Apparently, it is a recessive genetic condition that both parents must carry in order for albinism to occur.

When we had Emerson, we went full-steam ahead into learning all we could about albinism. There is a support organization called the National Organization for Albinism and Hypopigmentation (NOAH). What a lifesaver. They gave us the names of other children and adults with oculocutaneous albinism. There are national conferences that are attended by people who want to know more about the condition that my sons have, along with people with various types of albinism. The first thing we learned is that the word "albino" is a hurtful, slang name that we need to educate people not to use. The correct term is albinism. If you do nothing more than wipe the word albino out of your vocabulary, our story has found its purpose. The correct word to use is albinism.

It is necessary to connect with the school districts' early intervention program when the child is a baby to ensure the support of professionals. The school provides vision, occupational, speech, physical, behavioral, and cognitive therapists. Also, a must is to make sure protective eyewear and hats are worn by people with albinism, and these items have to be 100 percent UV protective against the sun's harmless rays. We have found a company that sells infant eyeglass and sunglass frames with lenses dark enough to allow our sons to enjoy being outside. Our boys are fine indoors, and some people with albinism are fine indoors, as well. Our boys happen to be sensitive to light outside, so they have to wear dark glasses outdoors.

To recap: join NOAH, join professional groups through school districts, keep teachers informed, and wear UV-protected (UV-A, -B, and -C) glasses for protection.

To finish, our story we'd decided to have a second child, knowing there was about a 25 percent chance our new baby would be born with albinism. We had a beautiful baby boy, Fionn. Yes, he has oculocutaneous albinism, like his brother, Emerson; however, one fortunate thing is, our boys, throughout their lives, can and do support each other.

Also, we are members of the Unitarian church, where we have found support and love. The members are family, and the extended family has helped us tremendously to get through the tough times.

CHAPTER 23

Sleep Apnea

Michael Schwartz

I NEVER KNEW I WAS snoring. If you had asked me, I would have told you no, of course not, but my wife would have told you something different.

I was snoring. I had a lack of energy, and by the time the afternoon came around, I would just run out of gas. It was also hard for me to lose weight and I consistently had blood pressure issues. My doctor, who also has sleep apnea, insisted I go through the testing process.

I was told that people with this condition stop breathing in their sleep, and I was registering eighty-seven events per hour where I actually stopped breathing. The thing is, when you stop breathing for just ten seconds, you are in danger of stopping altogether. Also, your body then allows brain cells to die because it is going into a natural defense mechanism; it gets the feeling it's in a struggle. The pancreas also starts producing insulin, and if it's not being used, this is when people become diabetic as well. In the meantime, your liver wants to produce sugar and gets stored as fat, which makes it difficult to lose weight because it is producing while you're sleeping. And let's not forget high blood pressure. So, hearing all that was enough to scare me into getting tested.

Just recently I was diagnosed with obstructive sleep apnea, where the tongue blocks the airway and stops the breathing altogether. The testing included an overnight stay at a clinic that was basically a wired hotel: probes are attached to your body; and doctors run electrocardiograms (EKG) and do checks on your rapid-eye-movement (REM) sleep and breathing patterns. The tests are used to get an idea of how deep your sleep is, which is difficult for people with sleep apnea. If you can remember your dreams, you are probably experiencing REM sleep, which I was not. That night, it was difficult to sleep because of the process, but doctors were able to gather enough data over a five- to six-hour period that I would get about eighty-seven events per hour and that my oxygen was dropping to a low of 73 percent. After review, the doctors told me that if I didn't take care of this, my sleep apnea would kill me.

I had to go back to the clinic for another overnight stay, this time for a continuous positive airway pressure (CPAP) titration. This test was the set-up for the machine that I would live with to help me breathe. There are different machine and mask options, but you have to be able to breathe through your nose while keeping your mouth shut, and if that becomes a problem, there are chin straps. Luckily I don't need that, but in essence, this machine is forcing air into your lungs through the nose, bypassing the throat. It's all about personal preference, but I chose the nose pillows because they are smaller and I felt that was the best.

During the night, doctors were able to adjust the pressure of the air blowing in, along with the temperature. That night I actually had a good night's sleep, and I was sent home the next morning with my machine.

Now I can go to sleep and wake up in the same position I fell asleep in; it's like you can literally fold the corner of the blanket back into place like I was never there.

It's amazing how many guys I now know who also have sleep apnea, which is common for men over fifty. If I didn't do the treatments, I would be walking a fine line of potentially never waking up in the morning. Now I'm hoping to achieve a more active life and maintain better shape. I notice I have more energy throughout the workday, and although it's still too early to tell, it has already helped me keep up the pace.

If you need to get tested, stick with it because some try it and don't want to stay at it, but you need to; you have to learn to live with it. There are many options available, so find a machine that works for you. Even if it takes a week, a month, or two months, keep working until you get used to a breathing machine. I keep mine next to my nightstand so it's washed in the morning after use and then ready to go again at night. The potential downside of not treating sleep apnea is worse than the inconvenience of the breathing machine.

If anything, I would have gone about my treatment sooner. I've had these symptoms for about ten years, and when I think about it, I believe I could have been more active and in different shape, but that's hard to say for sure.

Today, I feel rested, have more energy, and have a reduction in leg pain (my achy legs were not able to come to a rest at night; something I believe is also due to blood flow). Sleep apnea is not painful, but it is treatable and you need to look after it. I have met a lot of people who use a breathing machine, and it has changed their life.

CHAPTER 24

Throat Cancer

David Manville

I HAVE BEEN THROUGH FOUR different voices, with four different sounds: my original voice, my voice after cancer, my voice after surgery, and then another voice after a second surgery.

In 2001, I was diagnosed with chondrosarcoma, an extremely rare cancer, on my vocal chords. Gradually, my voice decreased to a squeak before I finally lost my voice altogether and began having a hard time breathing. I would have to take a real, deep breath to get any of my voice back. At the time, my wife, Terry, was able to talk to a good friend of hers who was a speech therapist, and she knew that what I had was a tumor. I called my doctor and within twenty minutes, I was told to come to the office that afternoon.

After an MRI, a malignant tumor was discovered, and that's when my wife and I lost it. Terry was upset because I had been a smoker most of my life, and now I had no voice, but I knew I didn't want to rely on a machine to live. What I really think that scared her most, though, was that we had a special whistle between us, and without a voice, I would never be able to do that again.

I also decided to see a holistic doctor, who started me on a regimen of taking herbs and vitamin shots two to three times a week. I was also going to the gym and started rocking to beat this cancer.

The following week, I went in for a biopsy and had a tracheal tube put in for four months. As a gardener and a man of the outdoors, it was difficult for me to enjoy the activities I loved, like swimming; I couldn't go underwater. On top of that, I was told the tracheal would never come out; I think that was when I lost it. However, Terry and I refused to accept that answer and refused to have my vocal cords taken out. I felt that "the big guy upstairs" would do something to intervene.

Although I couldn't go underwater with the tracheal tube, my love for water allowed me to wade in the pool, but the hardest part of the summer was not being able to swim. I golfed, kept busy with my two acres of land, and gardened, but in my head, I decided I was going to beat this cancer.

In the meantime, we heard about a "miracle worker" at the Mayo Clinic in Minnesota, and we were able to get an appointment the next month. I was told my stay would be for a week, but when I got there, I received the news that they would be able to take care of the cancer while leaving my vocal chords intact and removing the tracheal tube. My surgery was then scheduled for September 13, 2001, with a flight on September 11, but for whatever reason, my surgeon booked his flight from Denver to Minnesota on September 10 instead, while we drove to the clinic. I still remember what a ghost town it was driving through Chicago because of the tragic events on 9/11, and for the first time ever, the original doors to the Mayo Clinic were closed that day.

The cancer, which had grown over my airways, was restricting my vocals chords from reverberating, but they wouldn't have to remove them. I swear I heard the doctors say he scraped off all the cancer he could so that I would still be able to breathe and hopefully talk. Four days later I did, and the next day I was released.

A few weeks after, I went back to work and back to the clinic to get the tracheal tube removed. Two days after that, I jumped right in my pool, something I wasn't able to do since June. Everything healed well, and I had to go back to the Mayo Clinic twice a year for check-ups. It turns out in 2005 the cancer came back, which is common for this form of cancer; it could have been anywhere from five to ten years later. The danger, though, was that it blocked the airways, and this time I was devastated because I thought for sure I wouldn't have a voice.

I had the same surgery where they scraped out the cancer, but the recovery was a lot shorter this time because of the vitamins, herbs, and being in shape. Although when I learned there was the possibility of losing my voice, the first thing I thought of was to make a tape recording saying "I do" to give my only daughter away in marriage. I don't think I ever told my daughter or even my wife that, but I wanted that as my last speech.

By trade I'm a social worker, so I think the Big Guy kept my voice for a reason. Now I'm talking and I'm teaching, and he wants me to say something, so I must be good at what I do, I figure.

At my last check-up, the doctors said things looked good, and while I'm not cured of cancer, I can live a long time with this form of cancer. It doesn't spread, but it's there, and I'm always conscious of it, especially when I eat or drink certain foods. On a day-to-day basis, I know the cancer's there, and at least once a day, when I look in the mirror, those scars remind me.

I also continue to exercise and bench-press two hundred fifty pounds at least four to five days a week, eat organic and all-natural products, and take my vitamins and herbs. If you ask people who know me, I have one of the most positive attitudes; I don't believe in negativity or dealing with people who suck the life out of you. Really, I don't need the drama because life's too good, in the last eleven years especially, I've had an entire new way of looking at life. There are only certain things in life you have control over, as in my cancer, all I can do is take care of myself by being physically and mentally strong.

As it turned out, four years later my cardiologist found a leak in my left heart valve, working my lungs overtime. The shocking part was, though, that I didn't have any symptoms, even if I was close to having a heart attack. I hit the gym even harder and had surgery for a double bypass and a new valve. The first thirty days after was spent building strength, walking three to four miles, and weightlifting. I was only supposed to add weights in small amounts, but I did more, and nine months later, I broke down and cried because I was benching two hundred pounds.

It's all about attitude. Terry has been through a lot, and her take on things is that these are just setbacks. It's made us stronger, and she has always been there to take care of things. If I didn't do the surgeries for my cancer, I'd be talking out of a box and I wouldn't be able to do my work. It's difficult to picture this because I love my job and love working with people. I don't think I'd be here without it because what else is there to do when you've done this all your life and you can't talk?

Before I was diagnosed, I wasn't aware of things such as healthy eating, exercise, and spirituality. After more than ten years now I have a focus on food, exercise has definitely changed, and so has my attitude. Get the attitude in check because the outlook is the most important, which is not any different for any disease. You can beat anything for a while, but you can't control it, so make the best out of what you have and enjoy what you can. That's just another reason I like advising, teaching, and talking, because of what I've been through.

I've been through three major surgeries and don't have regrets in life; I refuse to have them. But the worst thing I ever did as a kid was start smoking. Even now I have slipped here and there; it's still a struggle. It doesn't play a part in this form of cancer because it is genetic, but it sure has affected my heart. Chondrosarcoma cancer affects three-year-olds up to healthy athletes in great shape, so where's the correlation?

Overall, my therapy involves getting my hands dirty in my garden, doing my woodwork, and a lot of solidarity, and my life is great. I think I'm quite healthy, working and doing what I love, and everything is going the way it's supposed to. I feel good and wake up looking forward to the day.

CHAPTER 25

Thyroid Conditions

Dawn Peters

ANYTIME YOU HEAR THE "C word" you act emotional, but in a lot of ways, it is like a business decision: you need to know the right thing to do in order to get the job done right. In a lot of ways, that is the approach I took when I was diagnosed with thyroid cancer.

The symptoms for me started with a urinary tract infection; however, the medication I was prescribed I was allergic to, which created bumps on my neck. My doctor felt the best thing to do was to check my thyroid, and it turned out you could feel the tumor. The strange part was, though, the doctor figured out I probably had the tumor for about a year before I was officially diagnosed (mind you that was in 1988, when I was only twenty-four years old).

You see, if there is one thing "nice" about thyroid cancer, it is that this form does not tend to spread. Even so, both thyroids were removed on each side because, like any cancer, you just do not want reoccurrence. So three weeks later, my surgery was scheduled at the University of Michigan, and then about three days later, an iodine scan to check the procedure was performed to make sure the cancer had not spread. That was my last treatment; there has been no reoccurrence since, and at age forty-two I am cancer free.

Since my diagnosis, I have also had two children, and while the levels in women's body chemistry changes, I have not had any problems with pregnancy. I also continue to monitor my thyroid in order to stay healthy.

In terms of cancer, I had the "best" kind with the best outcome. I say this because I feel fortunate how mine was simpler and straightforward, as opposed to what the cause and treatment were; unfortunately, that is not the case for everyone, so it is important to be informed. We know what is best for us and our bodies, but the tricky part of having cancer is figuring that out. I took the surgery route because I was young, the tumor was aggressive, and it needed to be taken out right away. At the time, I also had what turned out to just be fatty-tissue removed too, which had been caused by stress.

In order to remain healthy, I take a daily vitamin, receive a blood test each year, and exercise three to four times a week through walking, tennis, or biking. I like to change up my workout routine with weights and Pilates as well so I do not get bored. There is also a high risk of bone mass being affected by thyroid cancer, so I make sure I do not end up with osteoporosis and do so with regular check-ups.

And with any kind of cancer, it is always best to research doctors and specialists who are rated high, which my parents helped me do. I found the right specialist for me at the University of Michigan Hospital, which was involved with my particular cancer, which is important.

Looking back now, I realize that what I went through was really nothing compared to others. However, without the treatment, they do not know whether the tumor would have spread; we can only assume it would have.

I think it is important to be informed of the doctors. For me, it was through the help of a book about alternative forms of treatments and choices. It showed me how to prepare, how to be informed, and which questions to ask. The book also helped my family with their emotions and taught them how to be supportive. I would also recommend at least three alternative opinions on your diagnosis. I was lucky because I had a simpler cancer with only one treatment, so I moved through the medical system well without getting the runaround, but a lot is really based on how your appointment feels.

My life was not dramatically different before my diagnosis, but you need to make those necessary lifestyle changes. I was certainly more stressed, which I believe makes a person more susceptible to disease; I do not know about cancer, but you need to make changes to reduce stress in your life. Most importantly though: exercise, eat right, and follow your gut regarding your own body.

Jamie Bear

At fifty-four years old, I am finally in control of my thyroid condition.

It as been a long path to discover what was wrong with me. I first noticed my larger neck when I was about thirty-eight. I knew it was not weight gain because I had not gained in any other part of my body. I went to my doctor, and she indicated my goiter was enlarged. She filled out a requisition for TSH blood tests. After she reviewed the tests, she indicated my thyroid blood levels were within normal range. So I was told to do nothing and she would check during my yearly check-up.

After about three years there was no change in my thyroid levels, but my neck was getting thicker and thicker. I could not wear turtlenecks or anything around my neck. Not much else was going on, so I guess I just kept on going with my normal life. My doctor noticed my goiter was getting larger after about four years, and after blood tests (normal again), she put me on 25 milligrams of Lexitroid to see if that would decrease my goiter.

The first day I took the medicine I went crazy; I thought I was going to lose my mind. I was so edgy that I walked out of my house without shoes, in the middle of winter, and walked down the block. I was out of control. Needless to say, that was the last pill I took.

The good news is that my doctor sent me to an endocrinologist. I walked into the office, and he could not believe the size of my neck. I immediately knew I had someone who cared. He did an ultrasound, blood work, and a needle biopsy to see if I might have cancer. He explained so much to me that I could not believe I had not seen him sooner. Specialists are what they say: *specialists*. I feel doctors who specialize are the ones to go to if you notice anything unusual. General practitioners don't seem to want to send you (the money) away, so they pretty much try to treat conditions instead of making a referral; time is wasted. If I had had cancer, what would those four years have meant to my quality of life?

I had a choice to remove my thyroid or go through radiation treatment and keep my thyroid working. I felt that anytime you remove anything from your body, other complications can occur. So I went through radiation, and my thyroid goiter shrank. I was put on medicine to maintain my thyroid levels and have continued yearly exams. Wow, to have a normal size neck again.

I am still weary about wearing turtlenecks, but not as much. I am always feeling my neck for a lump, but at least now I know what to do. I maintain yearly check-ups with my endocrinologist, blood tests every six months, and an occasional ultrasound. One thing I recently learned is that if your Vitamin D levels are not kept within normal range, people with my condition can develop additional conditions like Crohn's disease; it is necessary to always get your Vitamin D levels checked along with your thyroid levels. I had a Vitamin D count of eight. Normal range starts at thirty. I have been taking three Vitamin D pills of 400 milligrams each, and now my count is thirty-one.

So far, so good. Sorry, general practitioners; I will always go to a specialist.

Sarah Bear

I never thought I would be telling my story regarding my thyroid at age twenty-three.

I had never thought of my thyroid gland as anything to be concerned about.

I am fortunate to have a very knowledgeable mother. She is living with thyroid issues. She was told it was passed down from some relative on one side of her family. Her take on this is that no one on either side of the family wants to own up to it or is aware of it. Anyway, my mom's specialist told her that her children needed to have their thyroid levels checked at least once a year. It is more common in women, but men can and do have low or high levels that can affect their thyroid. One is never too young to have a base-level test.

I went to my general practitioner, who was happy to write out an order for blood testing. It came back normal. During this time in my life I was having issues with my metabolism; I was always tired. In addition, I have hair loss issues. My mom decided to make an appointment for me to see her specialist, and lo and behold I have the start of a goiter, which can lead to cancer. I then had an ultrasound and am now on thyroid medicine to keep my levels up and allow my thyroid gland not to have to work so hard to keep my levels normal.

It is important to get your thyroid levels checked and then push on to get a specialist's diagnosis when your body is not functioning well, there are other symptoms, and there is a family history of thyroid problems.

Understand, your thyroid will work harder to produce the necessary hormones to keep your body levels normal. The human body is an incredible machine. Our body tries very hard to keep us normal. So my advice is to always insist on blood work, and be persistent to make sure your body is actually keeping things normal. Again, pay attention to other symptoms and family history.

Pay attention to what your body is trying to tell you. That is not to suggest that a person should be a hypochondriac, but that it is necessary to keep in touch with your body. That will inevitably lead to a more knowing, positive way of life.

❧

Ken Bear

Life started in Wisconsin. My father was a Presbyterian minister, and during his tenure we lived in many towns in Wisconsin. My family, with two brothers and two sisters, grew up very loving and full of action. As a teenager, I was diagnosed with a heart problem that required open-heart surgery. Even so, I worked summers to help pay my way through Kalamazoo College in Michigan. One summer, I even worked in a foundry.

After college, I continued a vigorous life. My wife, Susan, whom I met at college, and I were both interested in pursuing a life in the theatre. We were both accepted at the Dallas Theatre Center in Texas and completed a rigorous three year master's program in theatre. Neither of us had the temperament for professional theatre, so I took teaching jobs that made it possible to teach theatre courses and direct plays.

It was in the late eighties, while I was teaching at Fountain Valley School in Colorado Springs, that I became overly fatigued. After many tests, it was discovered that my thymus was the culprit. I didn't realize until later that the removal of my thymus was a contributor to my myasthenia gravis (MG; a chronic autoimmune neuromuscular disease characterized by varying degrees of weakness of the skeletal (voluntary) muscles of the body) later in life. The thymus gland is situated in the center of the upper chest just behind the sternum (breastbone). It is in the thymus that lymphocytes multiply and become thymus cells (T cells).

Then it was the late nineties, and I was forty-seven years old. I was diagnosed with MG; the early removal of the thymus gland made matters worse. My advice: don't get your thymus removed during adolescence. If I had known this, my life would be closer to normal. With MG, early death is a possibility.

At that time, my daughters were young; I was determined not to leave them. My symptoms included eyes that would not stay open, extreme weakness, and low resistance to diseases due to my weakened immune system. I also had to wear an eye patch to rest my one weak eye. This was hard on my little girls and people would stare at me and laugh; I was the pirate.

My specialist helping with my MG has been excellent. My symptoms are, for the most part, under control.

What do I do beyond medicine? I keep very busy. I remain a full-time theatre director/teacher at Ripon College in Wisconsin where I remain focused on my work and students. It leaves me little time to dwell on my MG. I also strive to reduce necessity for steroids, while keeping my MG in control. My diet is vegetarian to reduce my fat intake, and it helps save the planet too.

Keeping this fine balance is required and takes constant adjusting. This may include taking more or less of my steroids, making sure I have time for naps, and keeping my alcohol intake to a minimum (one beer instead of two).

My goal is to keep a positive attitude and laugh a lot. Fortunately, I can still find humor in the ups and downs of life.

CHAPTER 26

Viral Disease

Kathleen Bear

HEAVENS YES, I CAN SAY now at age fifty-three that my previous lifestyle was completely different before I was diagnosed with hepatitis C, which progressed into cirrhosis of the liver, and five years ago the diagnosis of the end-stage of liver failure. And to really understand how, I have to start from the beginning.

In the seventies, I was using drugs and sharing needles (yes, I even tried heroine, but soon stopped because I did not care for it); however, this was all before the time where AIDS was a worry. Soon I realized that alcohol was cheaper than drugs. I later was working at a mom-and-pop bar, where I became a heavy drinker. It seemed like the times were getting longer and longer to get over a hangover, so an eventual routine check-up led to blood tests that revealed why I was not feeling so well.

I took the appropriate tests and was officially diagnosed with hepatitis C in 1991. From there I tried an injectable drug called Interferon alfa-2b, which turned out to be unresponsive. I was also suffering from depression (I mean, who would not be with this kind of situation as a single mom with a seven-year-old child?), so that meant I was not a candidate for many other medications or even a transplant. But I was eventually put on water pills, diuretics, Lasix, and Aldactone. In turn, I ended up in the hospital a lot, and once you are an inpatient, you really become a number.

The University of Michigan Hospital recommended a procedure called TIPS (transjugular intrahepatic portosystemic shunt), which goes into the jugular vein and uses a form of a shunt to help get the ammonia out of your liver. So the TIPS procedure is like a filter that has to be removed and replaced from time to time.

Today though, I can proudly say I have been sober for twelve years. I also continue to take my medications that I drink in order to move my bowels (mind you, I have lost fifty pounds in the process) and cleanse out my system, and that is what keeps me alive. There are some side effects, such as memory loss and lack of concentration, but an overload of ammonia in my liver is not good, either. All in all, my philosophy was (and is), if it was not working, I needed to do something different. And as long as I take care of myself and do my diuretics and Lasix in the morning, I feel pretty good. I drink a lot of water and I walk everywhere too; I do not even drive anymore.

Basically, I do all this or I die.

Death, however, is not an option right now. I have a twenty-eight-year-old son (who will hopefully give me grandchildren), and my church family, who is my support, is important to me. As an adopted only child, you need to have that.

Without this treatment I would be dead right now; heck, I even had the doctor sitting right in front of me telling me *it didn't look good*. But death was not part of my game plan at all.

My advice is to be your own advocate; it is not good enough to be just the patient, you have to know about it. I read, I researched, and I became informed, and that led me to come to the conclusions that looked like promising ways to go. I felt like a rubber ball being bounced back and forth, so I made sure to really turn my life over because I am the one with this disease, and it is my body, like it or lump it.

I do have my bad days, and those are the days I stay close to home, but I want to be a participant in the parade, not just the one who watches from the side. Having support (which included AA), changing my whole life around, and not hanging around anyone who drinks alcohol has made me the healthier person I am today.

♋

Doug Holder

It was in May 2007 that what I thought was just a feeling of being lethargic actually turned out to be a diagnosis of a more complex strain of MRSA, also know as a staff infection.

When I first got those feelings of being run down, I knew it was not right and was time to go to the doctor. Soon after that, I was rushed to a nearby hospital for hydration. I was released afterward, but I probably didn't have the full blood work that needed to be done. I say this looking back, thinking while I was at home that I had been an incubator for this disease to emerge.

Thereafter, I was admitted, through the emergency room, into the University of Michigan Hospital, where I was tested for spinal meningitis. It turns out that was not the case, but a staff infection had gotten into my heart valves. The infection turned them into mush, which meant they had to be replaced. For about a month and a half I was on antibiotics that went right to my heart; however, my infection also went into my brain stems, which caused about a 90 percent loss of their function. Even after all I have been through, I now just have to take high blood-pressure medication.

For me, that first warning sign was being lethargic, and I am glad I could get the special treatment I did because that care saved my life. Now at age fifty-three, it is strange to think back about how I was also in the medical sales field for more than fifteen years; that is the weird part.

So far, things are better. Yes, I take blood-pressure medicine, and lately Coumadin for my heart, but things are better than can be expected and certainly more than I deserve. I say that because when you go through something like this, you find your worth and measure other than in material things.

Now I exercise by doing things like yard work in my Hamburg Township, Michigan, home and taking a walk. I also try to eat better. Although I am thankful for my treatment, and the things I have been through, because without it, I would not be here. I have been very fortunate, but at the same time, I question what is going on and what lies ahead. I feel I am going through a transition.

So I say my note to all of you is to treat your neighbor as your brother and try to find the good in each other, because coincidently, your brother is one of the harder people to have a relationship with. Life is a mystery, and the first step toward discovery comes after you die.

I think my lifestyle was not different prior to my diagnosis, but I do think I was transitioning over the last ten years. I became disillusioned with business and how people were treating one another (I kept my mouth shut when I thought I should), which was strange considering I was taught to stand up for myself and speak my mind.

I have always held on to faith, and that is what I have to hold. I think that this is a mini-train facilitating us for our next life, and I think our spirit comes back and we become more aware. It all stems from one golden rule: treat people right.

ABOUT THE AUTHOR

ANDREA KING is a Metro Detroit-based journalist, writer, and photographer. She is the product manager and lead writer of *Patient Stories*, along with the publicity coordinator of the National Alliance on Mental Illness (NAMI) metro chapter. King, an experienced reporter for many community newspapers and websites, is a frequent contributor to the *Detroit Free Press, Detroit Metromix,* and *Ambassador Magazine.* She lives in Northville, Michigan, but keeps active running marathons, traveling the world, and scavenging local boutiques. You can reach her at www.patientstories.com. This is her first book.